THE FOURTH DELUXE COLLECTOR'S EDITION OF

DAN DARE
PILOT OF THE FUTURE
PRISONERS OF SPACE

**ANOTHER COMPLETE FACSIMILE OF AN EARLY
DAN DARE ADVENTURE FROM EAGLE
COMPILED BY**

MIKE HIGGS

HAWK
BOOKS

DAN DARE
Prisoners of Space
FIRST EDITION

ISBN: 0 948248 42 4

Published by
HAWK BOOKS LIMITED
SUITE 309
CANALOT STUDIOS
222 KENSAL ROAD
LONDON W10 5BN

Dan Dare Copyright © 1990 Fleetway Publications.
This arrangement Copyright © 1990 Hawk Books Ltd.
Concept & Design: Mike Higgs Graphics.
Printed in England.

FOURPENCE-HALFPENNY

EVERY FRIDAY

EAGLE

28 MAY 1954 Vol. 5 No. 22

DAN DARE
PILOT OF THE FUTURE
PRISONERS OF SPACE

LUCKY STEVE VALIANT! YOU'RE A "CERT" TO WIN THE EARTH GOVERNMENT AWARD FOR THE ACE CADET AT TOMORROW'S PASSING OUT.

I WISH I FELT AS SURE AS YOU DO, TONY.

WHICH OF YOU BLIGHTERS PINCHED MY SPATIAL GAZETEER?

AT THE ASTRAL TRAINING COLLEGE ATTACHED TO SPACE H.Q., THREE SENIOR CADETS —STEVE VALIANT, TONY ALBRIGHT AND MARK STRAIGHT— ARE PREPARING FOR THE NEXT DAY'S PASSING OUT PARADE.

IT'S TIME YOU TRADED THAT SIEVE FOR A *REAL* HEAD, MARK! YOU LOANED YOUR GAZETEER TO YOUNG SPRY — GENIUS OF THE JUNIOR SCHOOL — LAST WEEK.

"FLAMER" SPRY'S BUILDING A MODEL OF COLONEL DARE'S NEW "PERFORMING FLEA" —THAT HUSH-HUSH JOB THEY'VE JUST TAKEN OFF THE SECRET LIST.

THE BOFFINS SAY DAN DARE WILL BE ABLE TO DO A SOLO PATROL OF THE ENTIRE SPACE-STATION PERIMETER — RIGHT OUT TO VENUS AND BACK — IN THAT CRATE.

THAT KID PROMISED TO RETURN MY BOOK NEXT DAY. FAG!

HEY, TUBBY POTTS! CUT ACROSS TO JUNIOR SCHOOL AND TELL SPRY IF HE'S NOT HERE IN TWO TICKS WITH MY BOOK, I'LL HAVE HIS RED SCALP FOR A BOOT-BRUSH.

STRAIGHT AWAY, STRAIGHT!

AS THE BOYS PREPARE FOR THE ANNUAL CEREMONY, SIR HUBERT GUEST AND COLONEL DAN DARE DISCUSS A MATTER OF GRAVE IMPORTANCE AT SPACE H.Q.

PEGASUS, OF THE TRANSPORT FLEET, WAS DUE IN FROM VENUS AT 17·03 HOURS YESTERDAY. SOMEWHERE HERE, IN AREA X, OUR COMMUNICATIONS ROOM LOST CONTACT. EMERGENCY PATROLS WENT OUT IMMEDIATELY, BUT FOUND ABSOLUTELY *NOTHING*. BRIEFLY, THE *PEGASUS* HAS VANISHED IN SPACE.

WHICH MAKES FIVE SHIPS LOST ON THE VENUS RUN IN AS MANY WEEKS. IT REMINDS ME OF THE OLD DAYS WHEN WE FIRST TRIED TO REACH VENUS . . .

. . . THE *PEGASUS* TYPE WAS SPECIALLY BUILT FOR THE VENUS TRADE. THERE'S NOTHING WRONG WITH THE DESIGN OR CONSTRUCTION —I TESTED THE FIRST ONE OFF THE ASSEMBLY LINE MYSELF. COULD IT BE SABOTAGE, SIR HUBERT?

OUT OF THE QUESTION, DARE—EVERYONE CONNECTED WITH THE OPERATION HAS BEEN THOROUGHLY VETTED. WE'RE UP AGAINST A NEW AND UNKNOWN FACTOR!

OR A *HIDDEN* ENEMY, SIR?

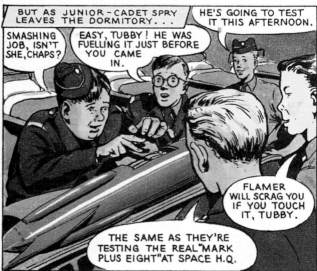

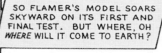

CONTINUED

FOURPENCE-HALFPENNY

EVERY FRIDAY

EAGLE

4 JUNE 1954 Vol. 5 No. 23

DAN DARE
PILOT OF THE FUTURE
PRISONERS OF SPACE

!

DOWN, SIR !

GOWK !

ON THE EVE OF THE PASSING OUT CEREMONY AT ASTRAL TRAINING COLLEGE, "FLAMER" SPRY, A JUNIOR CADET, GOES TO THE STUDY OF STEVE VALIANT, TONY ALBRIGHT AND MARK STRAIGHT TO RETURN A BOOK. DURING HIS ABSENCE, OTHER JUNIORS ACCIDENTALLY LAUNCH "FLAMER'S" SUPER MODEL OF DAN DARE'S NEW SPACE-CRAFT, THE "PERFORMING FLEA". THE LITTLE ROCKET BURSTS THROUGH THE DORMITORY ROOF, SOARS SKYWARD AND CRASHES TO EARTH, NARROWLY MISSING DAN DARE AND SIR HUBERT GUEST, WHO HAVE BEEN INSPECTING THE REAL "PERFORMING FLEA".

SOMEBODY'S GOING TO PAY FOR THIS OUTRAGEOUS PRANK !

WHAT THE DICKENS IS IT ?

WATCH IT, SIR — IT MIGHT BLOW UP !

JUST LOOK AT THIS ! IT'S A PERFECT SCALE MODEL OF MY NEW JOB, THE "PERFORMING FLEA" — AND STILL HOT !

I'LL MAKE IT HOT FOR SOMEBODY AND GIVE HIM A FLEA IN HIS EAR FOR THIS !

IT CAME FROM OVER ASTRAL COLLEGE WAY, I THINK, SIR.

THAT CONFOUNDED THING MIGHT HAVE KILLED US ! WE'LL GO STRAIGHT OVER TO ASTRAL AND RUN THE CULPRIT TO EARTH.

DON'T BE TOO TOUGH ON HIM, SIR — A BOY WHO CAN BUILD A JOB LIKE THIS, DESERVES EN-COURAGEMENT.

THE OWNER OF THIS DIABOLICAL INSTRUMENT WILL TAKE TWO PACES FORWARD . . .

LATER, THE PRINCIPAL OF ASTRAL ADDRESSES THE ASSEMBLED SCHOOL.

MARCH !

FOURPENCE-HALFPENNY

EVERY FRIDAY

EAGLE

11 JUNE 1954 Vol. 5 No. 24

DAN DARE
PILOT OF THE FUTURE
PRISONERS OF SPACE

A FINE WAY TO RUN A SPACE-FLEET, I *MUST* SAY! THIS BLOOMING CRATE'S ALL SET FOR FINAL TESTS AND NOW WE'VE GOT TO HAVE KIDS CLAMBERING ALL OVER HER—BAH!

GET INTO THE GRAVITY LOCK, FLAMER!

GOLLY, STEVE, ISN'T THIS WIZARD?

STOP BEEFING, GROUPIE, AND GIVE THE BOYS A CHANCE! I'M GOING BELOWSTAIRS TO RUSTLE UP A CUP OF CHAR.

FOR NEW READERS:

DAN DARE IS ABOUT TO SHOW STEVE VALIANT AND "FLAMER" SPRY OVER HIS NEW SOLO PATROL SPACE-SHIP, "THE PERFORMING FLEA", WHEN HE RECEIVES AN URGENT SUMMONS FROM SIR HUBERT GUEST. LEAVING DIGBY AND "GROUPIE" TO CARRY ON, DAN MAKES HIS WAY TO THE CONTROLLER'S OFFICE.

COLONEL DARE DESIGNED THIS SIMPLIFIED SYSTEM OF CONTROL HIMSELF. HE CAN GO TROUBLE-SHOOTING ANYWHERE IN SPACE—*ALONE*—IN THIS CRAFT, M'LADS!

PLENTY OF ROOM TO BRING BACK SURVIVORS FROM ANY ACCIDENT OR BREAKDOWN.

A BIT DIFFERENT FROM *YOUR* DAY, I GUESS, SIR!

I'LL SAY IT'S DIFFERENT! FLYING WAS AN *ART* IN THOSE DAYS. A MAN HAD TO USE HIS *OWN* BRAINS INSTEAD OF ONE OF THE ELECTRONIC GADGETS.

NOWADAYS, ALL A PILOT DOES IS LEAVE IT TO THE BOFFINS TO PLOT HIS COURSE ON THIS DEVICE, LIE DOWN NICE AND COMFY ON HIS TUMMY, THROW THIS MAIN CONTROL LEVER, THE JETS BLOW, HE TAKES OFF AND BEFORE HE KNOWS IT, HE'S *ARRIVED*!

JINGO! I WISH I WAS GOING ON THIS TEST FLIGHT.

THAT'S PROGRESS FOR YOU.

EVERYTHING'S HERE FOR AN EMERGENCY JOB — SPARE SPACE-SUITS, ALL TYPES OF SMALL ARMS, RATIONS . . .

LOOK OUT, VENUS, HERE I COME!

BOY! WILL I HAVE SOMETHING TO TELL THE BLOKES BACK AT ASTRAL!

MEANWHILE, IN SIR HUBERT'S OFFICE. COMMUNICATIONS ROOM REPORTS THEY'VE COMPLETELY LOST CONTACT WITH SPACE-STATION XQY. THE SIGNAL BROKE DOWN TEN MINUTES AGO.

THAT'S THE CONTROL POST FOR AREA X.

RIGHT! AND *THAT'S* THE AREA WHERE ALL FIVE OF THE VENUS TRANSPORT SHIPS VANISHED.

I'D BETTER GET CRACKING RIGHT AWAY, SIR!

DEAD LUCKY I PLANNED TO MAKE THE TRIAL RUN IN "THE PERFORMING FLEA" TO STATION XQY. THE COURSE HAS BEEN PLOTTED ON THE NEW ELECTRONIC PILOT, SO I CAN BE AWAY WITHIN THE HOUR.

IN THE BLAST-PROOF CHAMBER BELOW THE LAUNCHING-RAMP...

I'D BETTER TAKE SOME CHAR UP FOR GROUPIE AND THOSE KIDS.

OUTSIDE THE SECURITY FENCE ENCIRCLING THE TESTING GROUNDS AT SPACE H.Q., TONY ALBRIGHT AND MARK STRAIGHT ENVIOUSLY WATCH "THE PERFORMING FLEA".

LUCKY BLIGHTERS! I WISH COLONEL DARE HAD INCLUDED US IN HIS "PUNISHMENT", EH, MARK?

NO SUCH LUCK, TONY! BUT I GUESS STEVE WILL HAVE PLENTY TO TELL US.

WE'LL KEEP THIS QUIET UNTIL YOU'VE INVESTIGATED DARE. WE DON'T WANT THE PLACE BUZZING WITH RUMOURS.

YES, SIR. BETTER LET THE GROUND-STAFF CONTINUE TO THINK MY TAKE-OFF'S JUST THE ROUTINE TRIAL.

LOOK AT THAT YOUNG HERO!

BUT INSIDE "THE PERFORMING FLEA", ROUTINE IS ON THE WAY TO BEING SHATTERED IN A MOST UNEXPECTED FASHION!

COME OFF IT, YOU YOUNG DEMON!

WAKE UP, FLAMER!

I'LL TEACH HIM!

I'LL BRING HIM DOWN TO EARTH!

BUT GROUPIE'S ACTION HAS EXACTLY THE REVERSE EFFECT.

HEY — WHAT'S THE IDEA?

JUMPING JUPITER! WHAT'S THAT?

SUFFERING SATELLITES! LOOK, MARK!

COME ON, LET'S GET ROUND TO THE CONTROL TOWER! SOMETHING'S GONE HAYWIRE OUT THERE!

HAVE I GONE CRAZY, OR DO YOU SEE WHAT I SEE, SIR HUBERT?

THIS IS SHEER LUNACY! HOW ON EARTH...

"FLAMER" SPRY'S SMALL HAND HAS UNWITTINGLY STARTED A TRAIN OF EVENTS WHICH WILL PUT DAN DARE IN THE GREATEST PERIL OF HIS CAREER!

CONTINUED

FOURPENCE-
HALFPENNY

EVERY FRIDAY

EAGLE

18 JUNE 1954 Vol. 5 No. 25

DAN DARE
PILOT OF THE FUTURE
PRISONERS OF SPACE

B-BUT COLONEL DARE'S NOT *IN* THAT CRATE, MARK — WE SAW HIM PASS IN THAT GYROCOUPE A FEW MINUTES AGO!

YOU MEAN TO TELL ME THOSE TWO LADS FROM ASTRAL ARE IN THAT SHIP? I OUGHT TO GROUND YOU FOR THIS, DARE!

YOU'RE RIGHT, TONY! SOMEBODY'S PULLED A BONER — AND I'LL BET IT'S THAT YOUNG SCALLYWAG, "FLAMER" SPRY!

I DESERVE IT, SIR — I THOUGHT 1 COULD DEPEND ON DIGBY.

STEADY, DIGBY! IT'S JUST A BAD DREAM — YOU'LL WAKE UP IN A MINUTE!

THE STORY SO FAR:

WHILE "GROUPIE" IS SHOWING "FLAMER" SPRY AND STEVE VALIANT OVER DAN DARE'S NEW SHIP, "FLAMER" ACCIDENTALLY THROWS THE MAIN CONTROL SWITCH. FOR A FEW BRIEF MOMENTS "THE PERFORMING FLEA" STANDS ON HER JETS, THEN SCREAMS SKYWARDS ON HER PRE-PLOTTED COURSE TO SPACE-STATION XQY.

I HAD ENOUGH ON MY MIND WITH THE DISAPPEARANCE OF THOSE VENUS TRANSPORTS WITHOUT *THIS*!

IF ANYTHING HAPPENS TO THOSE BOYS, I'LL NEVER FORGIVE MYSELF.

COLONEL DARE, SIR!

MAY WE COME WITH YOU, COLONEL DARE? STEVE VALIANT'S OUR BEST PAL.

WHAT D'YOU SAY, SIR HUBERT?

ALL RIGHT — CLIMB IN AND KEEP QUIET!

WE CAN THANK OUR LUCKY STARS FOR *ONE* THING, SIR! THAT SHIP'S COMPLETELY ROBOT-CONTROLLED — EVERY INSTRUMENT WAS SET FOR THE TEST FLIGHT, SO NOTHING CAN GO WRONG UNLESS . . .

UNLESS SOMEONE INEXPERIENCED BEGINS MESSING ABOUT WITH THE CONTROLS!

A FEW MINUTES LATER.

I DON'T KNOW *WHAT* HAPPENED, COLONEL DARE, SIR. I WAS FETCHING UP SOME CHAR FROM THE BLAST-CHAMBER WHEN THE JETS BLEW AND KNOCKED ME COCK-EYED.

THERE'S ONLY ONE ANSWER. SOMEBODY PULLED THE MAIN CONTROL LEVER — AND IT WOULDN'T BE "GROUPIE".

THERE'S NOTHING WE CAN DO, SIR, BUT RETURN TO CONTROL AND WATCH HER COURSE ON THE TELEVIEWER.

I'D GIVE A GREAT DEAL TO KNOW WHAT'S GOING ON INSIDE THAT SHIP RIGHT NOW.

INSIDE THE STABILIZED HULL OF "THE PERFORMING FLEA"...

LET ME GET AT HIM!

NO PANIC, PLEASE!

JEEPERS!

YOU LITTLE CLOT — YOU'VE TORN IT PROPERLY THIS TIME!

TAKE IT EASY!

I—I'M SORRY, SIR, BUT YOU YANKED MY LEG WHILE I WAS HOLDING THE CONTROL-LEVER AND...

IT'S NO USE ARGUING WHO'S TO BLAME — WE'D BETTER TRY TO CONTACT SPACE H.Q. IMMEDIATELY FOR INSTRUCTIONS ON HOW TO ACT. WHERE'S THE TELECOMMUNICATION SYSTEM?

THE COMMUNICATIONS ROOM AT SPACE H.Q.

SHE'S KEEPING A TRUE COURSE, SIR HUBERT. I WISH WE COULD MAKE CONTACT WITH THEM AND TELL THEM TO LEAVE WELL ALONE. IF THEY START MEDDLING...

JUNIOR CADET SPRY'S A "DAB" AT ANYTHING TO DO WITH TELECOMMUNICATIONS, SIR.

TOPPED HIS FORM LAST YEAR.

AND IN "THE PERFORMING FLEA"...

ANY LUCK, "FLAMER"?

YOU GOT US INTO THIS MESS, M'LAD. YOU'D BETTER GET US OUT OF IT!

GOT A BRIEF SIGNAL A MOMENT AGO, BUT IT'S GONE. THIS TUNING SYSTEM'S A NEW ONE ON ME.

HOURS LATER, AS NIGHT FALLS OVER SPACE H.Q...

THERE'S STILL ABSOLUTE SILENCE ON THE XQY WAVELENGTH, SIR — BUT I'M GETTING SOME ODD FLASHES FROM THE POINT WHERE WE'VE PLOTTED "THE PERFORMING FLEA".

SHE SHOULD BE MAKING HER SPACEFALL AT XQY IN ANOTHER 40 MINUTES.

KEEP ON TRYING! IF YOU GET ANYTHING, INFORM ME AT ONCE — I'LL BE IN MY OFFICE.

EARTH H.Q. CALLING "PERFORMING FLEA"! IF YOU ARE RECEIVING ME, BUT UNABLE TO REPLY, HERE IS THE COMBINATION FOR SENDING. DEPRESS GREEN, BLUE AND YELLOW BUTTONS ON PANEL SIMULTANEOUSLY —EARTH H.Q. CALLING "PERFORMING FLEA"!

"DEPRESS GREEN, BLUE AND YELLOW BUTTONS SIMULTANEOUSLY..."

HOORAY! GOT IT!

A FEW MINUTES LATER, FOLLOWING INSTRUCTIONS ON THE SOUND CHANNEL, "FLAMER" SUCCEEDS IN ESTABLISHING VISUAL CONTACT WITH EARTH H.Q.

SORRY, COLONEL DARE! I SUPPOSE I'LL GET BOOTED OUT OF "ASTRAL" FOR THIS, BUT...

PIPE DOWN AND LISTEN! IN ABOUT HALF-AN-HOUR YOU'LL ARRIVE AT XQY...

...SOMETHING'S AMISS THERE — WE'RE GETTING NO REPLY TO OUR SIGNALS...

...DON'T HANDLE THE CONTROLS — "THE FLEA'S" ELECTRO-MAGNETIC DEVICE WILL TAKE HER STRAIGHT TO THE LANDING-DOCK. STAY IN THE SHIP UNTIL YOU ARE SURE THERE IS NO DANGER. CAPTAIN KING IS IN CHARGE OF THE CREW MANNING XQY — DO NOT DISEMBARK UNTIL YOU ARE SURE HE IS THERE AND ABLE TO ASSIST YOU.

CONTINUED

AS THE SPACE-CRAFT APPROACHES THE HUGE MAN-MADE SATELLITE, "GROUPIE" AND THE BOYS WATCH INTENTLY FOR SOME SIGN OF LIFE, BUT XQY IS AS STILL — AND AS SILENT — AS THE GRAVE!

FOURPENCE-HALFPENNY

EVERY FRIDAY

EAGLE

25 JUNE 1954 Vol. 5 No. 26

DAN DARE
PILOT OF THE FUTURE
PRISONERS OF SPACE

A PERFECT SPACEFALL, DARE! NO NEED TO WORRY ABOUT THE EFFICIENCY OF *THAT* SHIP.

IT'S THE BLACKOUT ON XQY'S SOUND AND VISION CHANNELS THAT BOTHERS ME, SIR. LET'S SEE IF HANK'S STILL IN TOUCH WITH YOUNG SPRY.

THE STORY SO FAR:

STEVE VALIANT, YOUNG FLAMER SPRY AND OLD GROUPIE ARE TRAPPED IN DAN DARE'S RUNAWAY ROCKET WHICH IS SPEEDING ON ITS ROBOT-CONTROLLED COURSE TO SPACE STATION XQY. AT SPACE H.Q., DAN AND SIR HUBERT WATCH ANXIOUSLY ON THE ASTROSCOPE AS THE "PERFORMING FLEA'S" ELECTRO-MAGNETIC LANDING DEVICE MAKES CONTACT WITH THE HUGE MAN-MADE SATELLITE AND THE SHIP CRUISES SMOOTHLY INTO THE RECEPTION BAY.

NO SIGN OF LIFE, GROUPIE!

NOT A SAUSAGE, STEVE!

SOMEONE'S ON DUTY! AIR-LOCK DOORS DON'T WORK BY THEMSELVES.

I DON'T LIKE THE LOOK OF THIS.

I'LL BREAK OUT THOSE SMALL ARMS — JUST IN CASE.

SOMEBODY'S MANNING THIS STATION. SEE? THE MAIN GAUGE IS CLIMBING TO EARTH ATMOSPHERE PRESSURE FAST!

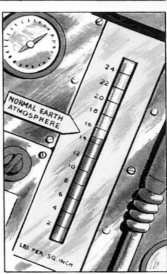

NORMAL EARTH ATMOSPHERE

LBS. PER SQ. INCH

AT SPACE H.Q.

STILL ON THE BEAM, HANK?

CALL HIM UP!

YES — BUT GETTING NOTHING! THAT DARN KID'S WALKED OUT ON ME!

L-LOOK!

"CALLING CADET SPRY! CALLING CADET SPRY!"

WHAT FLAMER SEES ...

CAPTAIN'S UNIFORM! THAT'LL BE KING, C.O. OF THIS OUTFIT!

CONTINUED

DO THOSE GRIM, GREEN ARMS MEAN WHAT DAN SUSPECTS? HAVE EARTH'S ARCH-ENEMIES — THE MEKON AND HIS RENEGADE TREENS — OCCUPIED SPACE STATION XQY?

FOURPENCE-HALFPENNY

EVERY FRIDAY

EAGLE

2 JULY 1954 Vol. 5 No. 27

DAN DARE
PILOT OF THE FUTURE
PRISONERS OF SPACE

RED GAUNTLETS OVER GREEN HANDS! THEY CAN MEAN ONLY ONE THING!

THE MEKON'S SHOCK TROOPS! BUT HOW...?

THE STORY SO FAR:
Dan Dare's runaway rocket, the 'Performing Flea', arrives safely at space station XQY. Senior Cadet Steve Valiant and Junior Cadet Flamer Spry (of Astral College), accompanied by Groupie, see the body of Captain King, the station commander, lying in the landing bay. While Steve and Groupie go to aid the stricken spaceman, Flamer re-establishes communication with the Earth. Steve and Groupie are held up by two mysterious attackers. Dan, suspecting a trap, orders Flamer to lock the door of the 'Flea' and await developments. As Dan and Sir Hubert watch at Space H.Q., red gauntleted hands suddenly encircle Flamer's mouth,

WE DROVE THE MEKON INTO OUTER SPACE AFTER 'OPERATION MERCURY'. SOMEHOW HE AND HIS TRAITOROUS GANG HAVE COME BACK AND CAPTURED XQY. *THIS EXPLAINS* THE LOSS OF THOSE VENUS TRANSPORTS!

I BLAME *MYSELF* FOR THIS! I NEVER SHOULD HAVE LET THOSE LADS LOOSE IN THAT SHIP.

TOO LATE TO TRY TO FIX THE BLAME, DARE — *WHAT ARE WE GOING TO DO?*

MEANWHILE, IN THE 'FLEA', EVENTS HAVE TAKEN AN UGLY TURN...

LEGGO, YOU BRUTE!

BE STILL, *WORM!*

HUMAN FOOLS! THEY BREED COURAGE EVEN IN THEIR INFANTS!

I KNOW YOU! YOU'RE THE...

AT SPACE H.Q....

DAN! SOMEONE'S CALLING YOU FROM XQY — BUT HE'S OUT OF VISION!

"CALLING COLONEL DARE! COLONEL *DAN* DARE!"

THAT VOICE! IT'S — IT'S...

... THE MEKON!

WE MEET AGAIN, COLONEL DARE — FACE TO FACE. *BUT WITH TOO MUCH SPACE BETWEEN US FOR MY PLANS!*

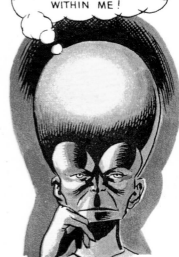

FOURPENCE-HALFPENNY

EVERY FRIDAY

EAGLE

9 JULY 1954 Vol. 5 No. 28

DAN DARE
PILOT OF THE FUTURE
PRISONERS OF SPACE

PUT IT PLAINLY, YOU GREEN FIEND!

ABUSE AVAILS NOTHING! MY PROPOSITION IS SIMPLE. SEND DARE — ALONE AND UNARMED — TO THIS PLACE AND I PLEDGE THE SAFE RETURN TO EARTH OF THE THREE PRISONERS.

WE'LL SEE YOU FILLETED FIRST, YOU LITTLE...

SILENCE, HANK! LET HIM FINISH!

THE STORY SO FAR :

Two Astral College cadets, Flamer Spry and Steve Valiant, accompanied by old Groupie, arrive at space station XQY in Dan Dare's runaway rocket, the 'Performing Flea', and fall into the hands of the dreaded Mekon and his traitorous Treens, who have captured the space station. On Earth, at Spacefleet H.Q., Dan Dare, Sir Hubert Guest and Hank finally succeed in contacting XQY, and watch the televiewer screen with shocked amazement as the Mekon appears and proposes his evil bargain.

I WILL REQUIRE THE SOLEMN OATH OF DARE AND SIR HUBERT THAT YOU WILL COMPLY WITH MY CONDITIONS. REMEMBER —ALONE—AND—UNARMED!

WAIT! BEFORE WE EVEN CONSIDER YOUR PROPOSAL, PROVE TO US YOUR CAPTIVES ARE ALIVE AND WELL!

SET THE EARTHLINGS BEFORE THE INSTRUMENT SO THAT DARE MAY SEE THEM!

YOU DO THE TALKING, STEVE!

HANDS OFF, YOU GRISLY GOON!

RIGHT, GROUPIE!

THEY LOOK IN GOOD SHAPE.

BUT FOR HOW LONG?

STEVE! ARE YOU ALL RIGHT?

NO BONES BROKEN YET, SIR, BUT I'M SORRY TO REPORT THAT THE CREW OF XQY HAVE HAD IT.

THE MEKON HAS THREE SHIPS ANCHORED ON THE FAR SIDE OF THIS STATION. THAT'S WHY YOU CAN'T SEE THEM ON THE ASTRO-VIEWER...

HANK! WATCH THAT PENCIL!

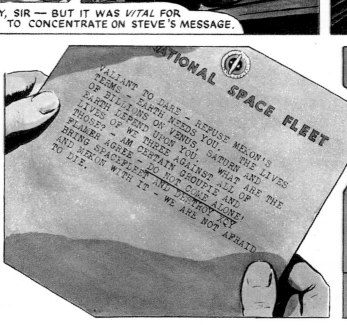

FOURPENCE-HALFPENNY

EAGLE

16 JULY 1954 Vol. 5 No. 29

THE STORY SO FAR:
Two Astral College cadets, Steve Valiant and Flamer Spry, accompanied by old Groupie, are prisoners in space on station XQY, which has been overwhelmed by the Mekon and his Treen shocktroops. The Mekon contacts Earth H.Q. on the televiewer in Dan Dare's runaway rocket, the 'Performing Flea', and offers Sir Hubert Guest a grim bargain: he will return his three captives to Earth if Dan Dare proceeds to station XQY *alone and unarmed*! While pretending to have lost his nerve, Steve taps out a message to Dare in morse, urging him to refuse the Mekon's offer and to attack XQY even though it means certain death to Flamer, Groupie and himself. With only two hours left to decide, Sir Hubert Guest calls an emergency meeting of Dan's closest friends.

YOUR NEW ASTRO-ARROW IS THE PERFECT JOB FOR A FAST TRIP OUT TO XQY — *AND* EASY FOR CADET VALIANT TO HANDLE ON THE RETURN JOURNEY. MAY I USE IT, SIR?

I'D LIKE TO REFUSE, DARE, BUT IF I DID, YOU'D FIND SOME OTHER WAY TO GO ON THIS — THIS LAST MISSION. TAKE HER — AND GOOD LUCK GO WITH YOU!

HANK! RUSTLE UP AN EMERGENCY GROUND-CREW AND GET SIR HUBERT'S PERSONAL SHIP READY TO TAKE OFF AT DAWN!

IT'S LIKE ASKING ME TO GET YOUR COFFIN READY, DAN — BUT I'LL DO IT.

DIGBY! GO TO MY QUARTERS AND LAY OUT MY SPACE-KIT!

YOUR *SHROUD*, YOU MEAN, SIR!

AT THE APPOINTED TIME, JUST BEFORE DAYBREAK, THE MEKON KEEPS HIS REMOTE RENDEZVOUS ON H.Q. TELEPANEL.

WELL, COLONEL DARE, HAVE YOU MADE YOUR CHOICE?

I LEAVE FOR XQY AT DAWN!

LET *ME* SPEAK TO THE GREEN BRUTE!

WHAT GUARANTEE HAVE WE THAT YOU WILL KEEP YOUR OATH AND SEND THE OTHERS BACK TO EARTH?

YOU HAVE NO CHOICE BUT TO ACCEPT MY WORD, SIR HUBERT. BUT BEFORE WE CLOSE THIS DEAL, YOU AND DARE MUST SOLEMNLY SWEAR THAT HE COMES *ALONE* — *WITHOUT WEAPONS*.

I SWEAR TO COMPLY WITH YOUR CONDITIONS, MEKON!

I ALSO — SO HELP ME!

I WILL ARRANGE A FITTING WELCOME FOR THE DISTINGUISHED EARTH COLONEL. HE HAS THWARTED MY PLANS *FOR THE LAST TIME!* THAT IS ALL!

AS THE MEKON'S IMAGE FADES FROM THE SCREEN, HANK ARRIVES TO REPORT.

ALL SET FOR THE TAKE-OFF, COLONEL DARE!

ON MY WAY, HANK!

WE'LL COME AND WISH YOU — ER — BON VOYAGE, DARE.

AS DAWN BREAKS AND THE STARS FADE, DAN DARE SETS OUT ON WHAT THREATENS TO BE HIS LONE, LAST JOURNEY INTO SPACE! WHAT FATE AWAITS HIM IN THE DEEP REACHES OF THE REDDENING SKY?

WHERE'S OLD DIGBY? I FOUND ALL MY KIT LAID OUT, BUT NO SIGN OF HIM.

I GUESS DIGBY'S LIKE ME — HE JUST CAN'T BEAR FINAL GOODBYES.

CHIN UP, PROFESSOR!

FOURPENCE-
HALFPENNY

EVERY FRIDAY

EAGLE

23 JULY 1954 Vol. 5 No. 30

DAN DARE
PILOT OF THE FUTURE
PRISONERS OF SPACE

Astral College Cadets, Steve Valiant and Flamer Spry, with old Groupie, are prisoners of the Mekon on Space Station XQY. The Mekon declares he will return his three captives in exchange for Dan Dare, alone and unarmed. Dan accepts the bargain. The Astro-Arrow bearing Dan rockets off.

THERE GOES THE GAMEST GUY WE'LL EVER KNOW.

AND THE GREATEST!

HE HAD NO FEAR — ONLY GREAT UNHAPPINESS BECAUSE DIGBY WASN'T HERE TO SAY GOODBYE.

RANK DISLOYALTY! SPACEMAN DIGBY WILL FIND HIMSELF ON AN OUTSIZE PEG BEFORE THIS DAY'S OUT!

SADLY DAN'S LOYAL FRIENDS LEAVE THE LAUNCHING-SITE AND RETURN TO H.Q. ADMINISTRATION BLOCK.

WE ARE HONOUR-BOUND TO SEND OUT NO PURSUIT SHIPS UNTIL DARE ARRIVES AT XQY AND THOSE LADS RETURN TO EARTH. BUT, BY HEAVEN, WHEN THEY DO, I'LL SEND EVERY SHIP AFTER THAT GREEN MONSTER — AND LEAD THE FIRST SORTIE MYSELF!

MEANWHILE, AT SPACE-STATION XQY, FLAMER SPRY IS BITTERLY ACCUSING STEVE VALIANT OF COWARDICE. STEVE, AWARE THAT TREEN GUARDS ARE LISTENING, STAYS DUMB, WHILE GROUPIE STAYS GLUM!

YOU SOLD DAN DARE OUT TO SAVE YOUR OWN WORTHLESS HIDE!

HOLD HARD, FLAMER —

FORGET IT, YOUNG 'UN! IF A FELLER CAN'T TAKE IT — HE JUST CAN'T TAKE IT!

WALLS HAVE EARS! I'D BETTER SWALLOW MY PRIDE AND PUT ON ANOTHER ACT FOR THE MEKON'S BENEFIT.

I'M SCARED, FLAMER! I'LL DO ANYTHING — EVEN TELL THE MEKON ALL ABOUT EARTH H.Q. DEFENCES IF ONLY HE'LL LET ME LIVE!

STEVE VALIANT — ASTRAL'S HEAD BOY! BAH!!!

ON THE FLAG-SHIP OF THE TREEN FLEET, THE EAVESDROPPING GUARD REPORTS TO THE MEKON.

GREAT ONE! THE ELDER BOY DISPLAYS A QUALITY WE HAVE NOT ENCOUNTERED BEFORE IN EARTH SPACEMEN. HE WEEPS — HE TEARS HIS HAIR AND VOWS THERE IS NOTHING HE WILL NOT DO TO SAVE HIS MISERABLE LIFE!

BRING HIM TO ME!

WHAT CAN YOU TELL ME OF EARTH'S DEFENCE PLANS?

I KNOW PLENTY! IF ONLY YOU'LL SPARE MY LIFE, I'LL DRAW YOU A DETAILED MAP OF THE LONDON H.Q. SET-UP.

WHAT'S THE USE OF US FIGHTING THE GREAT MEKON? YOU'RE BOUND TO BEAT US IN THE END!

GIVE THE YOUNG WHELP MATERIALS FOR WRITING AND DRAWING AND LOCK HIM UP ALONE!

SO BE IT, MASTER!

AT LAST ONE EARTHLING SPEAKS TRULY! WITH DARE IN MY POWER NOTHING CAN STEM THE FORWARD FLIGHT OF THE MEKON'S SCIENCE!

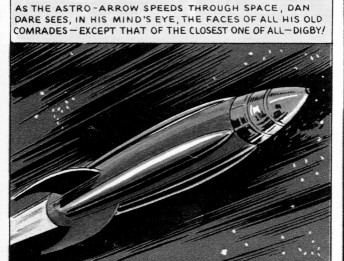

AS THE ASTRO-ARROW SPEEDS THROUGH SPACE, DAN DARE SEES, IN HIS MIND'S EYE, THE FACES OF ALL HIS OLD COMRADES — EXCEPT THAT OF THE CLOSEST ONE OF ALL—DIGBY!

IF THIS IS THE END, I'VE NO REGRETS. IT'S BEEN A GOOD LIFE — SURROUNDED BY LOYAL FRIENDS.

IF ONLY OLD DIGBY HAD BEEN THERE TO SHAKE MY HAND AND SAY . . .

"I'M A LADDIE FROM LANCASHIRE" ♪ ♫ ♩ ♯

WHAT THE DICKENS...?

DIGBY! WHAT DOES THIS MEAN?

IT MEANS I STOWED AWAY IN T'ARMS LOCKER, SIR. THE OLD FIRM'S TOGETHER AGAIN!

CONTINUED

UNDER OATH TO MEET THE MEKON ALONE AND UNARMED, WHAT CAN DAN DO TO KEEP HIS WORD?

FOURPENCE-HALFPENNY

EVERY FRIDAY

EAGLE

30 JULY 1954 Vol. 5 No. 31

DAN DARE
PILOT OF THE FUTURE
PRISONERS OF SPACE

SPACEMAN DIGBY! *DO YOU REALIZE WHAT YOU'VE DONE?*

AYE, SIR! I'VE PACKED THE ARMS LOCKER STIFF WITH EVERY WEAPON I COULD LAY MY TWO HANDS ON.. I'VE DESERTED, STOWED AWAY AND I'M A TRIPE-EARED, PUDDEN-FACED LANCASHIRE HOT POT —— APART FROM WHICH, *I FEEL REET' CHAMPION!*

THE STORY SO FAR : The Mekon, diabolical chief of the renegade Treens, has seized station XQY and holds Steve, Flamer and old Groupie as hostages against the life of Dan Dare, who has sworn to proceed alone and unarmed to XQY. Dan is speeding through space to keep his grim date when he discovers he is carrying a stowaway – a very resolute and heavily-armed stowaway – in the plump person of Spaceman Digby Fitzwilliam!

YOU'VE DONE *MORE* THAN THAT. YOU'VE CAUSED ME TO BREAK MY WORD OF HONOUR TO THE MEKON!

S-STEADY, SIR!

WE'VE GOT TO SET AN EXAMPLE OF TRUTH AND HONOUR TO THE REST OF THE UNIVERSE *AT WHATEVER COST* . . . AND NOW YOU'VE BROKEN FAITH!

THE WHOLE PURPOSE OF OUR PEACEFUL PENETRATION INTO OUTER SPACE HAS BEEN TO SHOW DWELLERS ON OTHER PLANETS THAT EARTH'S CODE IS THE FINEST WAY OF LIFE . . .

OH, DIGBY, DIGBY! *WHY* DID YOU DO THIS CRAZY THING?

BECAUSE *I* MADE NO PROMISE TO THAT THEER INHUMAN GRASSHOPPER —AND I *COULDN'T* STAND BY DOING NOWT WHILE YOU CHUCKED YOUR LIFE AWAY —*THAT'S WHY!*

YOU'VE THROWN YOUR *OWN* AWAY AS WELL NOW, OLD FRIEND.

WE'LL SEE ABOUT THAT! *HEY! WHAT ARE YOU DOING WITH THOSE GUNS, SIR?*

IF I'M TO KEEP TO THE LETTER OF MY OATH, I'VE NO OPTION BUT TO JETTISON THIS LOT.

FOURPENCE-HALFPENNY

EVERY FRIDAY

EAGLE

6 AUGUST 1954 Vol. 5 No. 32

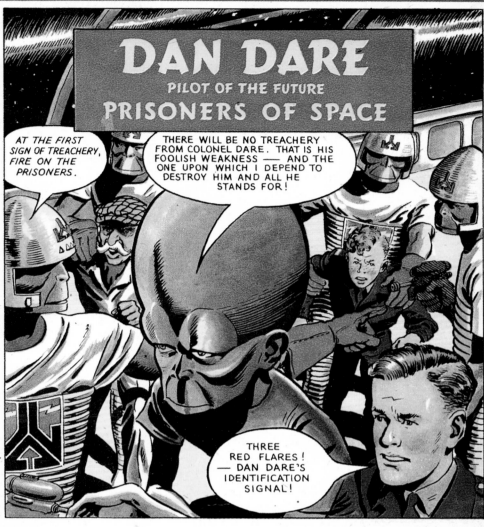

DAN DARE
PILOT OF THE FUTURE
PRISONERS OF SPACE

AT THE FIRST SIGN OF TREACHERY, FIRE ON THE PRISONERS.

THERE WILL BE NO TREACHERY FROM COLONEL DARE. THAT IS HIS FOOLISH WEAKNESS —— AND THE ONE UPON WHICH I DEPEND TO DESTROY HIM AND ALL HE STANDS FOR!

THREE RED FLARES! — DAN DARE'S IDENTIFICATION SIGNAL!

THE STORY SO FAR:
The Mekon, diabolical chief of the renegade Treens, has seized station XQY and holds Steve, Flamer and old Groupie as hostages against the life of Dan Dare, who has sworn to proceed alone and un-armed to XQY. Dan is speeding through space to keep his grim date when he discovers he is carrying a stowaway – a very resolute and heavily-armed stowaway – in the plump person of Spaceman Digby Fitzwilliam! Furious because his old comrade has caused him to break faith with the Mekon, Dan attempts to jettison the weapons which Digby has smuggled into the rocket-ship. In desperation, Digby squirts Dan with a paralyzing pistol and takes over the ship, which is now only a few minutes out from XQY where the Mekon waits.

YOU STINKER, STEVE VALIANT! HOW FAR WILL YOU GO TO SAVE YOUR YELLOW HIDE?

SILENCE, EARTH WORM! BECAUSE THIS ONE MAY BE USEFUL TO ME, HE ALONE WILL SURVIVE. YOU AND THE OLD ONE WILL BE PUT TO DEATH WITH DARE!

STEVE SHUDDERS WITH DISGUST AS THE MEKON'S SCALY HAND TOUCHES HIM, BUT STEELS HIMSELF TO CONTINUE HIS GAME OF BLUFF.

SO MUCH FOR HIS PROMISE TO FREE US IF DAN DARE SURRENDERED HIMSELF! I MUST PLAY FOR TIME.

I HAVE ALREADY DRAWN YOU THE PLANS OF SPACE H.Q., LONDON, AND I CAN DO MUCH MORE TO HELP YOU!

YOU ARE WISE FOR ONE SO YOUNG!

STEADY, YOUNG 'UN — DON'T SOIL YOUR HANDS ON A TRAITOR.

JUST LET ME GET AT HIM! I'LL TEAR THAT ASTRAL UNIFORM OFF HIS COWARDLY BACK!

IN SPITE OF THE TAUNTS OF FLAMER AND GROUPIE, STEVE SETS HIS JAW AND BIDES HIS TIME —

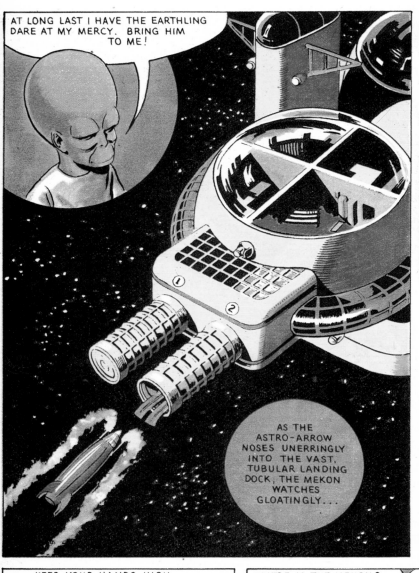

AT LONG LAST I HAVE THE EARTHLING DARE AT MY MERCY. BRING HIM TO ME!

AS THE ASTRO-ARROW NOSES UNERRINGLY INTO THE VAST, TUBULAR LANDING DOCK, THE MEKON WATCHES GLOATINGLY...

..WHILE INSIDE THE ASTRO-ARROW, DIGBY KILLS ALL LIGHTS AND TURNS FROM THE CONTROLS TO ADDRESS HIS CHIEF.

RIGHT ON TIME AND SMACK ON THE NOSE! YOU COULDN'T HAVE DONE BETTER YOURSELF, SIR!

UNTIE ME, YOU CRAZY CHUMP, AND I'LL TRY TO TALK THE MEKON INTO LETTING YOU RETURN WITH THE OTHERS!

MAKE NO MISTAKE, SIR — I'M STAYING PUT — RIGHT BEHIND YOU!

YOU KNOW I'VE GOT TO TELL THE MEKON OF YOUR PRESENCE — AND THAT WE'RE CARRYING ARMS. I'VE GIVEN MY OATH...

WE ALL MUST DO OUR DUTY THE WAY WE SEE IT, SIR — AND MINE'S TO SIT RIGHT HERE WITH MY TWO LITTLE POP-GUNS.

SO, TORN BETWEEN HONOUR AND FRIENDSHIP, COLONEL DARE STEPS OUT TO MEET THE MEKON.

KEEP YOUR HANDS HIGH, EARTHMAN!

TWO OF YOU SEARCH THE SHIP, WHILE I TAKE DARE TO OUR MASTER.

WHERE IS THE MEKON? I'VE SOMETHING VITAL TO TELL HIM.

FORWARD MARCH!

MEANWHILE, AS TREEN GUARDS SEARCH THE ASTRO-ARROW.

SWITCH ON THE LIGHTS!

HOLD YOUR FIRE UNTIL YOU SEE THE GREEN OF THEIR EYES, DIGBY LAD!

THIS'LL PARALYZE YOU, CHOOMS! TWO-GUN FITZWILLIAM RIDES AGAIN!

AS DIGBY GOES INTO ACTION, DAN IS MARCHED, AT RAY-GUN POINT, INTO THE MEKON'S PRESENCE.

KEEP YOUR HANDS UP!

GROUPIE — BOYS — ARE YOU ALL RIGHT?

SO WE MEET AGAIN...

...FOR THE LAST TIME!

COLONEL DARE!

DAN!

WAIT! IT IS MY DUTY TO TELL YOU THAT...

CAN DAN BRING HIMSELF TO SIGN HIS FRIEND'S DEATH WARRANT BY TELLING THE MEKON OF DIGBY'S PRESENCE IN THE ASTRO-ARROW? WATCH FOR NEXT WEEK'S SURPRISING TWIST!

FOURPENCE-
HALFPENNY

EVERY WEDNESDAY

EAGLE

13 AUGUST 1954 Vol. 5 No. 33

DAN DARE
PILOT OF THE FUTURE
PRISONERS OF SPACE

WHAT WERE YOU SAYING, COLONEL DARE?

UNDER THE TERMS OF MY OATH, I MUST WARN YOU...

STOP!

THE STORY SO FAR:

Dan Dare has sworn to go alone and unarmed to meet the dread Mekon on space station XQY. In return, the Mekon has promised he will free Flamer, Steve and old Groupie. On the journey, Dan discovers Digby has stowed away in the Astro-Arrow with a supply of arms. Dan tries to jettison the weapons, but Digby, determined to save his chief's life, stuns and binds him – then takes over the controls. On arrival at XQY, Digby releases Dan, who goes to keep his date with certain death. Treens search the Astro-Arrow, but Digby successfully ambushes them. Meanwhile, bound by his oath, Dan decides he must tell the Mekon of Digby's presence on the station, but before the words are out of his mouth . . .

TELL THE GREEN GRUB *NOTHING!* HE'S GOING TO DOUBLE-CROSS YOU!

SILENCE HIM!

HE'S — GLUB — GOING—TO—GLUG —KILL . . .

LET THE BOY SPEAK!

NOT UNTIL YOU HAVE FINISHED WHAT YOU BEGAN, COLONEL DARE. YOU WISHED TO WARN ME OF *WHAT* ?

DON'T TALK, DAN! THE SKUNK'S ALREADY SAID HE'S GOING TO KILL US *ALL* — EXCEPT STEVE !

AAAAH!

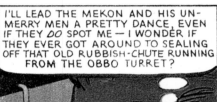

FOURPENCE-HALFPENNY

EVERY WEDNESDAY

EAGLE

20 AUGUST 1954 Vol. 5 No. 34

DAN DARE
PILOT OF THE FUTURE
PRISONERS OF SPACE

YOU MONSTER! YOU NEVER INTENDED TO KEEP YOUR WORD!

YOU'RE A FOOL TO EXPECT ME TO OBSERVE YOUR ABSURD CODE OF HONOUR, DARE.

THE STORY SO FAR:

Two Astral College cadets, Steve Valiant and Flamer Spry, accompanied by old Groupie, are captives of the Mekon on space station XQY. The Mekon promises to release them if Dan Dare goes immediately to XQY alone and unarmed. Dan takes off in the Astro-Arrow, not knowing he has a stowaway on board – Digby with an arsenal of small arms. Later, Dan attempts to jettison the weapons, but Digby tricks him and takes control. On arrival at XQY, Dan goes alone to meet the Mekon, who intends to double-cross him. While trying to warn Dan, Groupie is shot by a Treen ray-gun and the Mekon orders his chief guard to kill Flamer. Meanwhile, Treen guards who start to search Dan's ship are put out of action by Digby, who is now worming his way up a chute which is normally used for discharging rubbish-rockets . . .

LOOKS AS IF YOU'RE STUCK, DIGBY LAD – AND NEXT TIME ANYONE FIRES A RUBBISH-ROCKET, YOU'LL FIND YOUR-SELF OUT IN SPACE WITH THE REST OF THE TRASH!

STOP, MEKON! UNLESS YOU SPARE FLAMER'S LIFE, YOU'LL GET NO MORE INFORMATION FROM ME!

THERE ARE MANY WAYS OF MAKING A TRAITOR'S TONGUE WAG! ALREADY YOU HAVE PROVED THAT LIFE MEANS MORE TO YOU THAN EARTH'S RIDICULOUS CODE OF HONOUR.

GET ON WITH IT! I'D SOONER *DIE* THAN OWE MY LIFE TO A SQUEALING *RAT!*

ENOUGH! DESTROY THE EARTH CHILD!

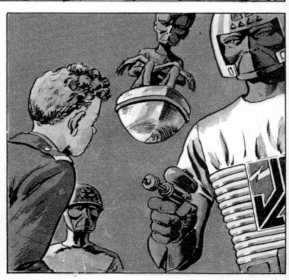

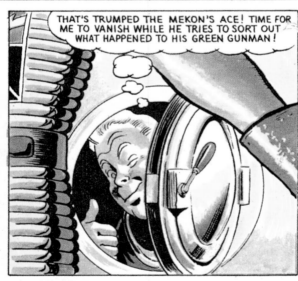

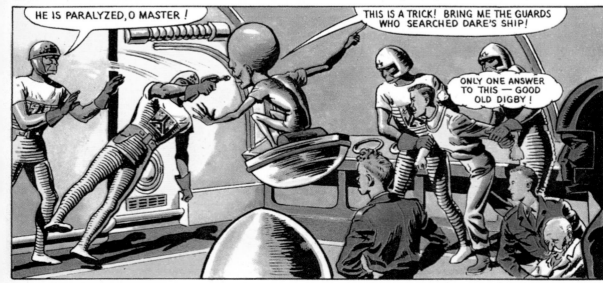

FOURPENCE-HALFPENNY

EVERY WEDNESDAY

EAGLE

27 AUGUST 1954 Vol. 5 No. 35

DAN DARE
PILOT OF THE FUTURE
PRISONERS OF SPACE

WE HAVE SEEN THIS BEFORE, O MASTER, ON BOTH VENUS AND MERCURY. *HE IS THE VICTIM OF AN EARTH PARALYZING PISTOL!*

DARE HAS BROKEN HIS OATH! HE SWORE TO COME ALONE AND UNARMED, BUT HE HAS BROUGHT BOTH ALLIES AND WEAPONS. *ALERT ALL GUARDS!*

WHAT'S FLAMER UP TO?

HERE I GO — *NECK OR NOTHING!*

THE STORY SO FAR:

On space station XQY, Dan Dare, Groupie and two Astral cadets, Flamer Spry and Steve Valiant, are captives of the dread Mekon, who has succeeded in double-crossing Dan. The Mekon orders his chief guard to destroy Flamer Spry with his ray-gun. Digby, who has wormed his way up the chute used for discharging rubbish-rockets into space, quietly opens the door and picks off the green gunman with his paralyzing pistol. Only Flamer sees Digby, who promptly begins his return journey to commence harassing operations elsewhere. While the bewildered Treens try to find the reason for the chief guard's sudden collapse, Flamer sees his chance to turn the tables still further!

I OVERESTIMATED YOUR SENSE OF HONOUR, DARE. *I WILL NOT MAKE THAT MISTAKE AGAIN!*

I'VE *GOT* TO HOLD THE LITTLE HORROR'S ATTENTION WHILE FLAMER DOES HIS STUFF.

I SWEAR I DID NOT KNOW I WAS CARRYING A STOWAWAY WHEN I LEFT EARTH!

KEEP HIM BUSY, COLONEL — I'M ON MY WAY!

YOUR TRICK AVAILS YOU NOTHING, FOR YOU WILL DIE AT ONCE! *SHOOT HIM!*

WAIT! BEFORE YOU REDUCE THE NUMBER OF YOUR PRISONERS STILL FURTHER, IT MIGHT BE A GOOD IDEA IF YOU COUNT THEM AGAIN — IF YOU *CAN* COUNT UP TO MORE THAN THREE!

FOOLS! THE EARTH-CHILD HAS ESCAPED!

HE MUST HAVE GONE THIS WAY, O MASTER!

MEANWHILE, FLAMER, LESS BULKY THAN DIGBY, IS MAKING A FAST JOURNEY DOWN THE CHUTE!

NEXT STOP WHERE?

AS THE TREEN SHOCK-TROOPS RUSH TO DO THEIR MASTER'S BIDDING, DIGBY REACHES THE BOTTOM OF THE CHUTE

SEARCH DARE'S SHIP!

COVER EVERY OUTLET! THERE ARE ENEMIES AMONG US!

MADE IT — BUT ONLY JUST!

... WHERE A WARM WELCOME IS WAITING FOR HIM!

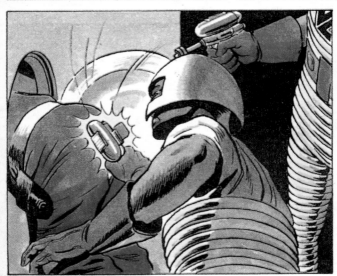

OUCH! A REAR ATTACK!

A MOMENT LATER . . .

DISARM HIM!

AH WELL, HOW BETTER CAN A MAN DIE THAN FACING FEARFUL ODDS?

ARRRRRGH!

CRUMBS! WHAT'S THIS?

MIGHTY MEKON!

I COULDN'T HAVE TIMED IT BETTER!

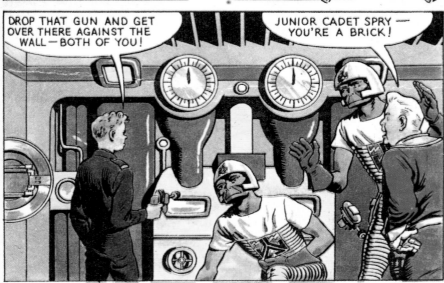

DROP THAT GUN AND GET OVER THERE AGAINST THE WALL—BOTH OF YOU!

JUNIOR CADET SPRY — YOU'RE A BRICK!

MEANWHILE, IN THE OBSERVATION TURRET . . .

YOU WILL NOT SURVIVE TO ASSIST THE ENEMIES IN OUR MIDST, DARE! DESTROY HIM!

THE GAME'S NOT PLAYED OUT YET, YOU MILDEWED MONSTER!

WITH DAN DARE FACING DEATH FROM THE TREEN GUARD'S RAY-GUN, AND DIGBY AND FLAMER FAR AWAY IN ANOTHER SECTION OF THE SPACE STATION, IT LOOKS AS IF ONLY A MIRACLE CAN SAVE THE GALLANT COLONEL. WATCH FOR NEXT WEEK'S EXCITING EPISODE!

FOURPENCE-HALFPENNY

EVERY WEDNESDAY

EAGLE

3 SEPTEMBER 1954 Vol. 5 No. 36

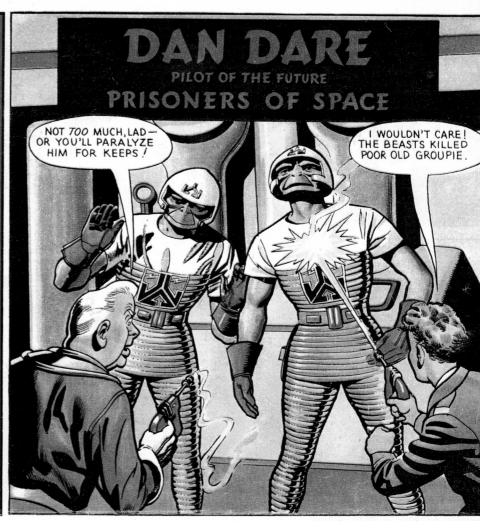

DAN DARE
PILOT OF THE FUTURE
PRISONERS OF SPACE

NOT *TOO* MUCH, LAD— OR YOU'LL PARALYZE HIM FOR KEEPS!

I WOULDN'T CARE! THE BEASTS KILLED POOR OLD GROUPIE.

THE STORY SO FAR:
Dan takes off in the 'Astro-Arrow' to free Groupie, Steve and Flamer, held hostage by the Mekon at space station XQY. Under oath to go alone and unarmed, Dan tries to jettison the weapons which stowaway Digby has provided, but Digby immobilizes him and takes control. On XQY, Flamer warns Dan that the double-crossing Mekon intends to kill them. Groupie is shot down by the Treen guards. After putting the Treens who search the 'Astro-Arrow' out of action, Digby climbs a rubbish-rocket chute and saves Flamer's life. Digby and Flamer escape down the chute and successfully tackle the Treens at the other end — but they will have to move very rapidly if they are to save Dan, who is about to be destroyed upon the orders of the Mekon.

WHAT'S THE DRILL, SIR?

JUST AS WELL I DID A TOUR OF DUTY ON THIS STATION AND KNOW WHERE TO FIND THINGS —*AND DON'T 'SIR' ME!*

KEY CONTRO

IF WE GIVE "CATSEYES" DARE A SPOT OF DARKNESS UP THERE, I RECKON HE'LL MAKE THE MEKON SEE STARS.

ON

ON

IN THE OBSERVATION TURRET ABOVE...

FAREWELL, COLONEL DARE — YOU HAVE THWARTED ME FOR THE LAST TIME!

THIS IS IT!

NO!

AS THE GUARD FIRES...

MASTER—THE LIGHTS!

GUARD THE DOOR!

GET HIM, YOU FOOLS!

A PRESENT FOR A BAD BOY!

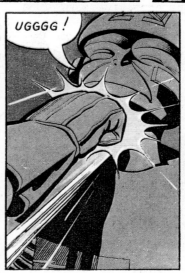

UGGGG!

CHIN UP, STEVE! I'LL BE BACK!

FOURPENCE-HALFPENNY

EVERY WEDNESDAY

EAGLE

10 SEPTEMBER 1954 Vol. 5 No. 37

DAN DARE
PILOT OF THE FUTURE
PRISONERS OF SPACE

GROUPIE! *YOU'RE ALIVE!*

STEVE VALIANT! JUST MY LUCK TO BE STUCK WITH *YOU!* YOU'D BETTER TELL YOUR PAL THE MEKON TO FINISH ME OFF.

THE STORY SO FAR:

The dread Mekon and his body of renegade Treens are searching all over space station XQY for Dan, Digby and Flamer Spry, who have escaped from the observation turret. The trio, who know that the double-crossing Mekon intends to destroy them if he possibly can, fight their way to Dan's 'Astro-Arrow', which lies in the reception bay, and succeed in putting out of action the Treens who are guarding the ship. Up above them, in the observation turret, a lone Treen guard is watching Steve Valiant, who has bluffed the Mekon into believing that he is a traitor to Earth. Steve, kneeling beside Groupie, who has been shot down by a deadly Treen ray-gun, realizes with a shock that the tough old-stager is *still alive!*

I'M *NOT* A TRAITOR, GROUPIE. YOU'VE *GOT* TO BELIEVE ME!

THEN HERE'S YOUR CHANCE TO PROVE IT. GET THAT TREEN GOON TO TURN HIS BACK ON ME FOR *TWO SECONDS!*

TAKE ME TO THE MEKON AT ONCE! I HAVE SOMETHING VITAL TO REPORT.

THE GREAT ONE ORDERED ME TO KEEP YOU HERE UNTIL HE RETURNS.

NOW OR NEVER!

NOW, STEVE!

STICK TO HIM, GROUPIE!

SHADES OF VENUS! THE DEAD ONE LIVES!

GRAB THAT GUN, LAD!

AS STEVE AND GROUPIE OVERPOWER THE GUARD, THE LIGHTS SPRING TO LIFE IN THE TURRET AND, AS GROUPIE TURNS TO LOCK THE DOOR, THE EFFECT OF DIGBY'S PARALYZING PISTOL BEGINS TO WEAR OFF THE CHIEF GUARD!

KEEP HIM COVERED WHILE I SECURE THE DOOR!

HE *CANNOT* BE ALIVE! *NONE* CAN SURVIVE A RAY-GUN'S BLAST!

STAY PUT, GREEN-BEAN!

MEANWHILE, DAN AND CO. HAVE RETAKEN THE 'ASTRO-ARROW' AND ARE PREPARING FOR ACTION.

LOOK! THE LIGHTS HAVE GONE ON IN THE "OBBO" TURRET!

DIG! GET ON THAT T-VIEWER AND CALL UP EARTH—PRONTO!

AYE, AYE, SIR!

EE, THEY'LL HAVE A SHOCK AT H.Q. WHEN THEY SEE DESERTER DIGBY!

CALLING EARTH! 'ASTRO-ARROW' AT XQY CALLING SPACE H.Q.

AT H.Q., DAN'S COMRADES ARE DISCUSSING HIS FATE—AND DIGBY'S MYSTERIOUS DISAPPEARANCE.

ZERE IS NO SIGN OF DIGBY ANYWHERE, SIR.

BAH! I EXPECT HE'S HIDING SOMEWHERE—DAREN'T SHOW HIS FACE BECAUSE HE DIDN'T TURN UP AT DAN'S TAKE-OFF!

FORGET DIGBY! IT'S DAN WE OUGHT TO BE WORRYING ABOUT. WHY HAVEN'T WE HEARD FROM XQY?

NO NEWS FROM THE MEKON IS BAD NEWS!

HOLD EVERYTHING! WE'VE GOT SPACEMAN DIGBY ON THE T-VIEWER—CALLING FROM STATION XQY!

WHAT?

DIGBY! WHAT ARE YOU DOING ON XQY?

I'M A.W.O.L., SIR—AND AS SOON AS WE'VE SORTED OUT THIS MESS-UP, COLONEL DARE'S GOING TO PUT ME ON A PEG FOR MUTINY, DESERTION, PIRACY, AND I DON'T KNOW WHAT. HE WANTS A WORD WITH YOU, SIR!

ATTABOY, DIG!

WE SHOULD HAVE KNOWN HE'D NEVER DESERT DAN!

I'VE GOT TO MAKE IT BRIEF, CHIEF! DIGBY STOWED AWAY—AND LUCKY FOR ME HE DID! THE MEKON'S DOUBLE-CROSSED US, GROUPIE'S A 'GONER' AND THE TREENS ARE HOLDING STEVE CAPTIVE IN THE "OBBO" TURRET. WE'VE ESTABLISHED A BASE IN THE 'ASTRO-ARROW'!

WHAT CAN WE DO TO HELP, DAN?

GET A FLEET OF THE FASTEST PURSUIT SHIPS STANDING BY TO TAKE OFF IMMEDIATELY YOU GET THE "GO" FROM ME. WHEN YOU DO GET IT, BLAST XQY CLEAN OUT OF SPACE!

I'VE HAD THE CRACK SQUADRONS WAITING TO SCRAMBLE EVER SINCE YOU TOOK OFF!

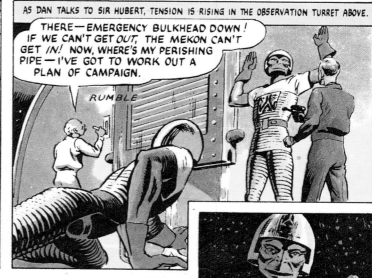

AS DAN TALKS TO SIR HUBERT, TENSION IS RISING IN THE OBSERVATION TURRET ABOVE.

THERE—EMERGENCY BULKHEAD DOWN! IF WE CAN'T GET OUT, THE MEKON CAN'T GET IN! NOW, WHERE'S MY PERISHING PIPE—I'VE GOT TO WORK OUT A PLAN OF CAMPAIGN.

RUMBLE

AH, THAT'S BETTER! MAYBE NOW I CAN FIGURE OUT WHY I'M STILL ALIVE AND KICKING.

MY GUESS IS THAT DAN, DIGBY AND FLAMER WILL MAKE STRAIGHT FOR THE 'ASTRO-ARROW'. IF THEY GET THERE, WE CAN...

LOOK OUT, STEVE!

AS THE GUARD RECOVERS FROM THE PARALYSIS CAUSED BY DIGBY'S PISTOL, HE ADVANCES MENACINGLY ON STEVE VALIANT. WHAT WILL HAPPEN? WATCH FOR NEXT WEEK'S THRILLING ACTION!

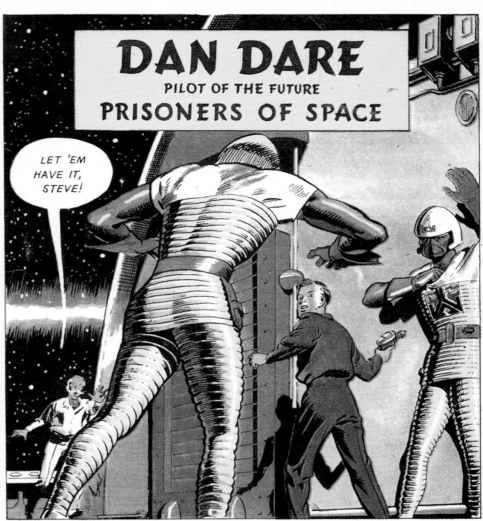

THE STORY SO FAR:
Trapped by the Mekon and his renegade Treens on space station XQY, Dan Dare, Digby and young Flamer Spry fight their way to their space ship, the 'Astro-Arrow', and contact earth H.Q. on the T-viewer. Meanwhile, in the observation turret, Groupie, who by some strange means has survived a deadly burst from a Treen ray-gun, helps Steve Valiant overcome the Treen guarding them. Groupie lowers the bulkhead and turns to see that the second guard, previously paralyzed by Digby's pistol, has recovered and is closing in on Steve. Caught between two fires, Steve swings around to face this new peril. Knowing that the gun he holds is death-dealing, Steve hates the thought of pulling the trigger and hesitates . . .

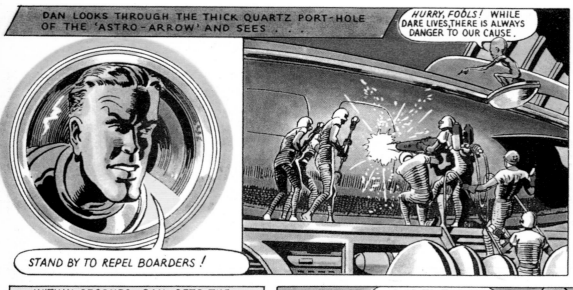

DAN LOOKS THROUGH THE THICK QUARTZ PORT-HOLE OF THE 'ASTRO-ARROW' AND SEES . . .

STAND BY TO REPEL BOARDERS!

HURRY, FOOLS! WHILE DARE LIVES, THERE IS ALWAYS DANGER TO OUR CAUSE.

WHAT IS IT?

SOME SORT OF OXY-RAY THAT'LL RIP OUR HULL APART IN A MINUTE OR SO!

NOT IF I CAN GET 'EM IN THE SIGHTS OF THIS NEW TELE-BROADSIDE.

WITHIN SECONDS, DAN GETS THE RANGE ON HIS ENEMIES . . .

THIS'LL STOP THEM IN THEIR TRACKS!

FLEE TO THE OBSERVATION TURRET!

AAAARGH!

GAAAARRK!

UUUGH!

JUST AS WELL I REMEMBERED TO SMUGGLE AMMUNITION ABOARD FOR THAT JOB.

IT'S DRIVEN THE BRUTES OFF — BUT FOR HOW LONG?

WHAT'S THE DRILL NOW, SIR?

WE'LL LEAVE FLAMER HERE AND HAVE A GO AT GETTING STEVE OUT OF THE "OBBO" TURRET.

WHEN DIG AND I LEAVE, SECURE THE DOORS AND STAND BY! YOU CAN COVER EVERY POSSIBLE POINT OF ASSAULT WITH THIS GUN. IF YOU SEE ANYONE COMING, DON'T HESITATE TO SHOOT!

UNLESS IT'S US!

AND JUST IN CASE THINGS GO WRONG, FLAMER . . .

DON'T SAY IT, SIR. WE'LL WIN OUT — SOMEHOW!

YOU BET WE WILL! I'VE GOT TO REPORT BACK TO H.Q. TO FACE CHARGES OF PIRACY, MUTINY, DESERTION, AND TAKING CHARGE OF AN 'ASTRO-ARROW' WITHOUT THE PILOT'S PERMISSION!

BUT AS DAN AND DIGBY PREPARE TO SET OUT ON THEIR DESPERATE SORTIE, ANOTHER PLAN IS BEING COOKED UP IN THE OBSERVATION TURRET FAR ABOVE!

WELL, THAT'LL KEEP HIM ON ICE FOR A WHILE! WHAT NOW, GROUPIE?

IF YOUR THEORY IS RIGHT AND DAN HAS RETAKEN THE 'ASTRO-ARROW', WE'D BETTER MAKE CONTACT WITH HIM.

D'YOU MEAN WE CAN TALK TO HIM FROM HERE?

WE MAY BE PRISONERS IN THIS TURRET, LAD, BUT WE'VE GOT THE MASTER CONTROL OF EVERY PART OF THIS STATION RIGHT HERE. I SHOULD KNOW, BECAUSE I WAS ONE OF THE SPACE PIONEER CORPS WHO ANCHORED IT OUT HERE TEN YEARS AGO.

THERE'S AN OVER-ALL P.A. SYSTEM HERE WITH SPEAKERS IN EVERY SECTION. IF DARE'S STILL ALIVE, HE'S BOUND TO HEAR US — AND IF MR GREEN-LUGS MEKON TUNES IN, I HOPE IT BURSTS HIS EARDRUMS!

HELLO! HELLO! THIS IS GROUPIE CALLING DAN DARE!

WILL GROUPIE'S VOICE REACH DAN AND DIGBY BEFORE THEY SET OFF ON THEIR DESPERATE RESCUE OPERATION? WATCH FOR NEXT WEEK'S EXCITING DEVELOPMENT.

FOURPENCE-HALFPENNY

EVERY WEDNESDAY

EAGLE

24 SEPTEMBER 1954 Vol. 5 No. 39

DAN DARE
PILOT OF THE FUTURE
PRISONERS OF SPACE

GROUPIE CALLING DAN DARE!

GROUPIE CALLING DAN DARE!

THE STORY SO FAR:
On space station XQY, Dan Dare, Digby and Junior Cadet Flamer Spry have escaped the Mekon's clutches and are in possession of the 'Astro-Arrow', in which Dan arrived from Earth. They have just beaten off an attack by the Mekon and his renegade Treens and are planning a sortie to the observation turret to rescue Senior Cadet Steve Valiant and bring out the body of old Groupie, who has been shot down by a deadly Treen ray-gun, when they are very astonished to hear . . .

GROUPIE TO DARE!

GALLOPING GALAXIES!

GROUPIE'S VOICE!

GROUPIE CALLING DARE!

G-G-GROUPIE'S G-G-GHOST!

IT IS THE VOICE OF THE OLD ONE WHOM WE KILLED. IF EARTH MEN CAN COME BACK FROM DEATH, OUR CAUSE IS LOST!

OBSERVATION TURRET

FOOL! WE SAW HIM DIE FROM A RAY-GUN BLAST. IT IS A TRICK!

TURN THE MAGNA-RAY ON THAT DOOR AND BURN IT THROUGH!

AS THE POWER-MAD MEKON'S TREENS BEGIN THEIR ASSAULT ON THE OBSERVATION TURRET DOOR, THE DIVIDED PARTIES OF EARTHMEN MAKE T-VIEWER CONTACT.

DARE TO GROUPIE! IF YOU ARE ALIVE, SHOW YOURSELF! OVER!

I'M ALIVE ALL RIGHT — AND TO PROVE IT, I'M HERE!

IT'S MIRACULOUS!

IT'S MARVELLOUS!

IT'S MAD!

AGAIN DAN DARE HAS GIVEN HIS WORD — AND THIS TIME TO A FRIEND. WILL THE 'ASTRO-ARROW' TAKE OFF SAFELY — AND WHAT DOES FATE HOLD IN STORE FOR STEVE AND OLD GROUPIE?

FOURPENCE-
HALFPENNY

EVERY WEDNESDAY

EAGLE

1 OCTOBER 1954 Vol. 5 No. 40

DAN DARE
PILOT OF THE FUTURE
PRISONERS OF SPACE

THE DOOR'S CAVING IN, BUT WE'VE GOT TWO RAY-GUNS, SO WE CAN HOLD THE FORT LONG ENOUGH FOR YOU TO GET AWAY.

GET MY SPACE-HELMET LIVELY, DIGBY!

AYE, AYE, SIR! IF YOU SEE A MOVE FROM THOSE CUSTOMERS, GIVE 'EM ANOTHER SQUIRT FROM YOUR PISTOL, FLAMER!

YOU BET!

THE STORY SO FAR:

Trapped by the double-crossing Mekon and his force of renegade Treens on space station XQY, Dan Dare, Digby and young Flamer Spry have recaptured the 'Astro-Arrow'. In the observation turret above, Steve Valiant and old Groupie who, miraculously, has survived a blast from a deadly Treen ray-gun, have locked themselves in. As the Mekon's guards assault the door of the "obbo" turret with a magna-ray drill, Groupie sets in motion the mechanism which operates the vast air-lock doors of the landing docks, thus clearing the path for the 'Astro-Arrow's' return flight to Earth. At the same time, Steve uses the T-viewer to get in touch with Dan and tells him that he must go back to Earth at once . . .

HAPPY LANDING, COLONEL DARE — AND TELL FLAMER TO REMEMBER ME TO THE CHAPS AT ASTRAL — SIGNING OFF—GOODBYE — AND GOOD LUCK!

WHAT'S THE DRILL, SIR?

LOOK OUT AT THOSE INDICATORS! GROUPIES OPENED THE DOORS OF *BOTH* BAYS. IF I CAN GET ACROSS TO BAY NUMBER ONE, I CAN PREVENT THE 'PERFORMING FLEA' FROM FALLING INTO THE MEKON'S HANDS.

TAKE OFF COUNT INDICATORS

BAY N°1   BAY N°2

AIRLOCK OPEN   AIRLOCK OPEN

LAUNCHING

PLUS 120

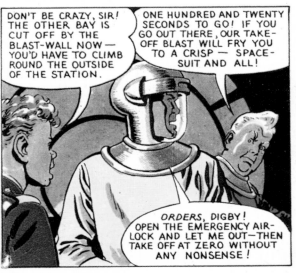

DON'T BE CRAZY, SIR! THE OTHER BAY IS CUT OFF BY THE BLAST-WALL NOW — YOU'D HAVE TO CLIMB ROUND THE OUTSIDE OF THE STATION.

ONE HUNDRED AND TWENTY SECONDS TO GO! IF YOU GO OUT THERE, OUR TAKE-OFF BLAST WILL FRY YOU TO A CRISP — SPACE-SUIT AND ALL!

ORDERS, DIGBY! OPEN THE EMERGENCY AIR-LOCK AND LET ME OUT—THEN TAKE OFF AT ZERO WITHOUT ANY NONSENSE!

TWENTY SECONDS LATER . . .

CRACK ON THE PACE, SPACEMAN! IT WON'T BE SO HEALTHY AROUND HERE IN A MINUTE OR SO!

AS THE VITAL SECONDS TICK AWAY, DAN DARE CLIMBS FURIOUSLY TO AVOID THE IMMINENT BLAST OF THE 'ASTRO-ARROW'S' JETS.

INDICATORS

BAY N°2

AIRLOCK OPEN

LAUNCHING

PLUS 5

AS THE INDICATOR REACHES ZERO...

WOOOSH

THERE SHE BLOWS! GOOD OLD DIGBY!

MEANWHILE, IN THE OBSERVATION TURRET...

THEY'RE SPACE-BORNE, GROUPIE!

STAND BACK, YOU GREEN GARGOYLES! YOU'RE A LITTLE TOO LATE!

TAKE THEM FROM THE REAR! USE THE CHUTE BY WHICH DARE ESCAPED. I MUST HAVE THE OLD ONE ALIVE TO LEARN HOW HE SURVIVED THE RAY-GUN.

MEANWHILE, DAN MAKES HIS WAY INTO BAY Nº1.

THANK GOODNESS THE BOFFINS DREAMED UP EXTERNAL CONTROL FOR THE EMERGENCY EXIT OF THIS LITTLE BEAUTY!

IF ONLY STEVE AND GROUPIE CAN HOLD OUT LONG ENOUGH FOR ME TO TAKE OFF, I MIGHT STILL SAVE THE SHIP — AND THEIR LIVES!

MEANWHILE, THE MEKON'S GUARD CLIMBS UP THE RUBBISH ROCKET-CHUTE TOWARDS THE OUTLET IN THE OBSERVATION TURRET...

DROP THOSE GUNS!

YOUR FIRST MOVE WILL BRING DEATH!

A MOMENT LATER...

I'M A CLOT TO HAVE FORGOTTEN THAT CHUTE DOOR, STEVE!

CHIN UP, GROUPIE! COLONEL DARE'S SAFE, AT LEAST!

CLOSE THE MAIN AIR-LOCKS AND SEARCH FOR THOSE OF US WHO ARE MISSING!

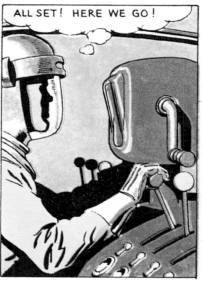

ALL SET! HERE WE GO!

MAIN AIRLOCK
OPEN
SHUT

WILL DAN DARE GET THE 'PERFORMING FLEA' SPACE-BORNE BEFORE THE VAST DOOR TO FREEDOM CLANGS SHUT? WATCH FOR NEXT WEEK'S EXCITING INSTALMENT!

FOURPENCE-HALFPENNY

EVERY WEDNESDAY

EAGLE

8 OCTOBER 1954 Vol. 5 No. 41

DAN DARE
PILOT OF THE FUTURE
PRISONERS OF SPACE

SCREEK!

JUMPIN' JETS — I'VE FOULED SOMETHING!

THE STORY SO FAR: Due to the heroic action of Steve Valiant and old Groupie, the 'Astro-Arrow', bearing Digby and Flamer Spry, gets safely away from space station XQY and speeds off towards Earth. Meanwhile, Dan Dare, determined to save the 'Performing Flea' from falling into the Mekon's hands, works his way across the outer shell of the vast man-made satellite towards launching bay number one, where the 'Flea' is docked. As Dan reaches his goal and throws the main control lever for take-off, the Mekon, in the observation turret above, orders his guards to close the air-lock doors leading to outer space.

LOOK, MASTER! IT IS THE SECOND EARTH SHIP!

I AM SERVED BY FOOLS! THIS IS DARE'S WORK!

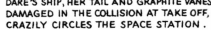

DARE'S SHIP, HER TAIL AND GRAPHITE VANES DAMAGED IN THE COLLISION AT TAKE OFF, CRAZILY CIRCLES THE SPACE STATION.

GOOD OLD DAN! HE'S PULLED OFF THE DOUBLE — SAVED THE 'FLEA' AS WELL AS THE 'ARROW'!

IT WASN'T A CLEAN TAKE OFF. HE MUST'VE BRUSHED THE DOOR. LOOK — HE'S LOST A TAIL VANE!

STILL UNDER POWER — BUT OUT OF CONTROL!

SEE, MASTER — HIS SHIP IS DAMAGED! HIS GRAPHITE VANES MUST BE JAMMED AND HIS COURSE FIXED...

...IN A TIGHT CIRCLE AROUND THIS SATELLITE! THE COLLISION HAS EITHER STUNNED OR KILLED DARE — BUT THIS TIME WE WILL MAKE CERTAIN! ESTABLISH CONTACT WITH MY FLAGSHIP!

THE THREE TREEN COMBAT SHIPS LIE ALONGSIDE XQY, HELD BY THEIR MAGNETIC GRAPPLING-DEVICES.

MEKON TO FLAGSHIP! ATTACK AND DESTROY EARTH-SHIP!

JET CONTROLS HAVE GONE, SO I CAN'T COMPENSATE FOR THE LOSS OF THAT GRAPHITE VANE! IF I CUT POWER, I'LL BE A SITTING BIRD FOR THE MEKON'S MURDERERS.

"TALK OF DEVILS" — AND THERE THEY ARE, SITTING SMACK ON MY TAIL! GET READY TO BALE OUT NEXT TIME ROUND, BROTHER DARE — AND HOPE FOR THE BEST!

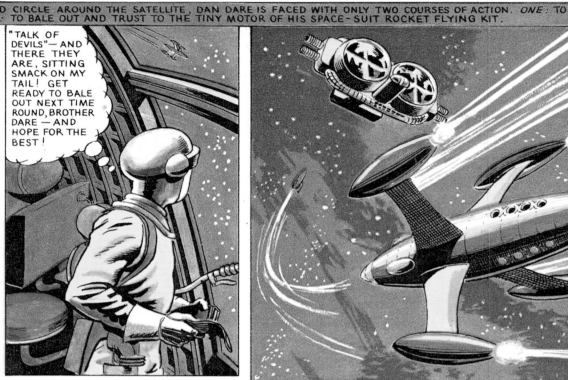

ENEMY IN SIGHTS!

HOLD FIRE — HE IS IN LINE WITH OUR OWN SHIPS! WAIT UNTIL HE IS CLEAR OF XQY.

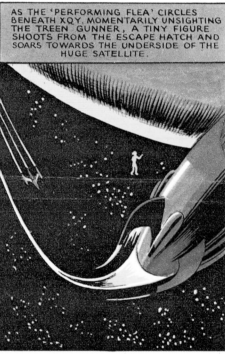

AS THE 'PERFORMING FLEA' CIRCLES BENEATH XQY, MOMENTARILY UNSIGHTING THE TREEN GUNNER, A TINY FIGURE SHOOTS FROM THE ESCAPE HATCH AND SOARS TOWARDS THE UNDERSIDE OF THE HUGE SATELLITE.

YOU NEED COVER — AND *FAST*, DANNY BOY — BEFORE THAT TREEN FLAK STARTS FLYING!

LET THE EARTHLINGS SEE THE END OF COLONEL DARE'S LITTLE DRAMA.

TEN SECONDS LATER . . .

VALE, COLONEL DARE.

GROUPIE — THE SWINE HAVE GOT HIM AT LAST!

SO THE BRAVE EARTH COLONEL ENDS UP AS COSMIC DUST SPINNING IN SPACE! AND NOW *YOU TWO* WILL PAY FOR YOUR STUPID INTERFERENCE WITH MY PLANS!

NOW, HOW THE HECK TO GET *IN*?

LOCKED OUTSIDE THE GIGANTIC SPACE STATION, CAN DAN DARE BREACH THE STRONGHOLD AND RESCUE HIS FRIENDS FROM THE SINISTER POWER OF THE MEKON? WATCH FOR NEXT WEEK'S EXCITING INSTALMENT!

FOURPENCE-HALFPENNY

EVERY WEDNESDAY

EAGLE

15 OCTOBER 1954 Vol. 5 No. 42

DAN DARE
PILOT OF THE FUTURE
PRISONERS OF SPACE

NOW DARE IS DEAD, THE FATE I HAD PLANNED FOR HIM SHALL BE *YOURS*.

THIS OVERGROWN TADPOLE'S TRYING TO SCARE US, STEVE.

WHAT A HOPE!

THANK HEAVEN THEY'RE BOTH STILL ALIVE.

THE STORY SO FAR:
Due to Steve Valiant and old Groupie, the 'Astro-Arrow', bearing Digby and Flamer Spry, gets safely away towards Earth. Meanwhile, Dan Dare, determined to save the 'Performing Flea' from the Mekon, works his way across the man-made satellite, XQY, to where the 'Flea' is docked. Just as Dan takes off, the Mekon orders his guards to close the air-lock doors. As a result, one fin is torn off and the 'Flea's course is set in a crazy circle around space station XQY. The Mekon sends a fighter to destroy Dan, but he bales out and reaches the station as the 'Flea' is blown to pieces.

STEVE FOOLED THE MEKON WITH THIS MUSTY OLD MORSE CODE, MAYBE IT'LL WORK A SECOND TIME.

TAP

MASTER! SOMEONE TAPS OUTSIDE!

SILENCE!

!?

IT HAS STOPPED. DOUBTLESS SOME FRAGMENTS OF DARE'S SHIP RAPPING ON THE HULL. OPEN THE OUTER AIR-LOCKS AND INSTRUCT MY FLAGSHIP TO ENTER!

HERE COMES THE BIRD THAT SHOT DOWN THE "FLEA". I HOPE THEY DON'T NOTICE THERE'S A CUCKOO IN THE NEST!

GROUPIE! THAT TAPPING WAS MORSE CODE. "D.D." — FOR *DAN DARE!*

YOU'RE DREAMING, STEVE! *NOTHING* COULD HAVE SURVIVED THAT TREEN SHIP'S ATTACK.

ACTING ON THE MEKON'S ORDERS, THE TREEN SHIP RETRACTS ITS FINS AND ENTERS THE LANDING DOCK.

"OPEN SESAME!" IF ONLY I CAN GET IN BEFORE "SESAME" CLOSES!

DAN DARE'S LUCK HOLDS GOOD, AND AS THE TREEN PILOT REPORTS TO THE MEKON...

MISSION ACCOMPLISHED, O MASTER! THE ENEMY WAS UTTERLY DESTROYED.

YOU HAVE DONE WELL, YOUR REWARD SHALL BE THE ORDER OF SEVEN MOONS.

I COULD PICK OFF THE FILTHY LITTLE GREEN GROWTH FROM HERE — BUT THAT WOULD MEAN INSTANT DEATH FOR STEVE AND GROUPIE. I'D BETTER BIDE MY TIME.

BRING FORTH THE SOLAR CELL WHICH WE PREPARED FOR DARE'S PUNISHMENT. NOW HE IS DEAD, I HAVE ANOTHER USE FOR IT.

AT ONCE, GREAT ONE!

A FEW MOMENTS LATER, THE TREEN SHIP'S CREW TRUNDLE A STRANGE OBJECT ON TO THE LANDING PLATFORM — A CLEAR, QUARTZ SPHERE, RATHER LIKE AN ENORMOUS BUBBLE.

BEHOLD, EARTHLINGS!

SHADES OF SATURN! WHAT HAS HIS WARPED MIND DREAMED UP THIS TIME?

WHAT IS IT, GROUPIE?

ASK ME! — BUT I'VE GOT A FEELING WE'RE GOING TO BE ON THE INSIDE LOOKING OUT BEFORE LONG!

THIS SOUNDS LIKE OUR LOT, STEVE.

NIL DESPERANDUM, GROUPIE! I STILL BELIEVE THAT RAPPING ON THE OUTER HULL WAS A SIGNAL FROM COLONEL DARE.

A "SOLAR-CELL"? WHAT NEW DEVILRY IS THIS? I'D BETTER CONSOLIDATE MY POSITION — FAST!

EARTHMEN! YOURS WILL BE THE HONOUR OF SHARING THE DESTINY I ARRANGED FOR DARE.

IN THIS SOLAR-CELL, YOU WILL BE LAUNCHED INTO SPACE. THE PROPULSION-UNIT IS SO DEVISED THAT YOU WILL ENCIRCLE YOUR BELOVED EARTH ON A FIXED ORBIT... A TINY MOON FOR-EVER SPINNING IN THE VOID! YOU WILL NOT DIE QUICKLY, FOR THE MECHANISM IS SET TO SUPPLY YOU WITH EARTH ATMOSPHERE CONDITIONS FOR TWELVE HOURS ONLY!

YOU DIABOLICAL MONSTER! IF YOU DO THIS BRUTAL THING, IT WILL BE OVER MY DEAD BODY!

PLAYING A LONE HAND AGAINST THE MIGHT OF THE MEKON, CAN DAN DARE RESCUE STEVE AND GROUPIE FROM THE DREADFUL DESTINY THE MEKON PLANS FOR THEM? WATCH FOR NEXT WEEK'S THRILLING EPISODE

FOURPENCE-HALFPENNY

EVERY WEDNESDAY

EAGLE

22 OCTOBER 1954 Vol. 5 No. 43

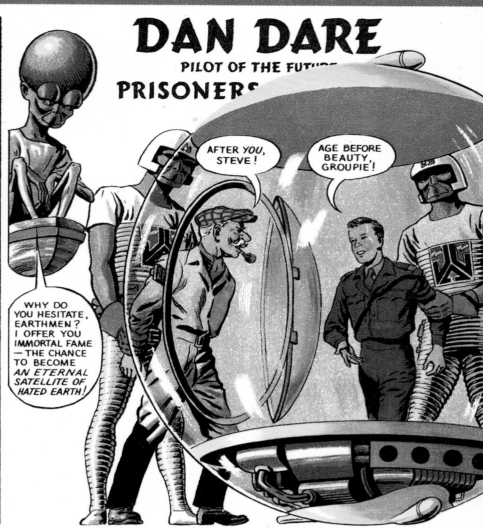

DAN DARE
PILOT OF THE FUTURE
PRISONERS

AFTER *YOU*, STEVE!

AGE BEFORE BEAUTY, GROUPIE!

WHY DO YOU HESITATE, EARTHMEN? I OFFER YOU IMMORTAL FAME — THE CHANCE TO BECOME *AN ETERNAL SATELLITE OF HATED EARTH!*

THE STORY SO FAR:

Believing that Dan Dare met his doom when the 'Performing Flea' was destroyed by the Treen flagship, the dread Mekon plans to imprison Senior Cadet Steve Valiant and old Groupie in a "solar-cell" and launch them into space from the man-made satellite XQY. The mechanism of the solar-cell is so contrived that the transparent sphere will circle Earth perpetually, like a tiny moon on a fixed orbit. A "space-snork" device ensures Earth atmosphere within the cell for *twelve hours only!* Dan Dare, who baled out from the 'Performing Flea's escape hatch in his rocket-powered space-suit, re-enters space station XQY when the outer air-lock doors are opened for the entrance of the Treen flagship. From his hiding place in the landing dock, he is watching and waiting his chance to rescue his friends and defeat the renegade Treens, as the Mekon unfolds his grisly plot.

WHAT *IS* THIS STRANGE QUALITY THAT MAKES EARTHLINGS JEST IN THE VERY FACE OF DEATH? I HAVE SEEN IT IN THE LATE COLONEL DARE — NOW *THESE* FOOLS SHOW IT ALSO.

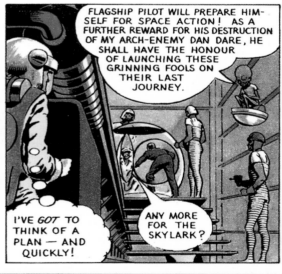

FLAGSHIP PILOT WILL PREPARE HIMSELF FOR SPACE ACTION! AS A FURTHER REWARD FOR HIS DESTRUCTION OF MY ARCH-ENEMY DAN DARE, HE SHALL HAVE THE HONOUR OF LAUNCHING THESE GRINNING FOOLS ON THEIR LAST JOURNEY.

I'VE *GOT* TO THINK OF A PLAN — AND QUICKLY!

ANY MORE FOR THE SKYLARK?

THE LITTLE MONSTER SAID STEVE AND GROUPIE CAN SURVIVE FOR TWELVE HOURS IN THAT BEASTLY BUBBLE. IF I CAN CONTACT EARTH H.Q., THERE MAY *STILL* BE A CHANCE.

LUCKY FOR ME DIGBY REMEMBERED TO SWIPE A FEW OF THESE LIMPET BOMBS — BUT *NOT* SO LUCKY FOR THE MEKON AND HIS MINIONS!

WHATEVER HAPPENS TO GROUPIE, STEVE AND ME, THE INSIDE OF THIS SHIP WILL BE A PRETTY UNHEALTHY SPOT IN EXACTLY TWELVE HOURS FROM NOW!

DAN SETS THE TIME-DEVICE ON THE SMALL BUT POWERFUL MAGNETIC BOMB. HE QUIETLY ATTACHES IT TO THE HULL OF THE TREEN FLAGSHIP, THEN SLIPS SILENTLY THROUGH A SMALL EMERGENCY BULKHEAD WHICH LEADS TO THE MAIN STAIRWAY.

NOW THAT THE MEKON THINKS I'M A DEAD DUCK, IT'S UNLIKELY THAT HE'LL HAVE POSTED GUARDS IN THE "OBBO" TURRET.

DAN'S HUNCH PROVES RIGHT, FOR HE FINDS THE TURRET DESERTED EXCEPT FOR THE DEAD GUARD.

MY LUCKY STAR'S WORKING OVERTIME TONIGHT! THAT'S ONE GREEN ENEMY LESS! I WONDER HOW HE GOT *HIS* LOT?

SATELLITE XQY CALLING EARTH H.Q.!

AT EARTH H.Q.

ANY NEWS, HANK?

NOT SINCE SPACEMAN DIGBY CALLED US FROM THE 'ASTRO-ARROW', SIR HUBERT. HE'S ON COURSE AND HOMING FAST.

POOR DIGBY! IT BROKE HIS HEART TO HAVE TO REPORT SEEING THE END OF COLONEL DARE. KEEP TRYING THE XQY CHANNEL. I'M GOING BACK TO THE ASTRO-VIEWER ROOM.

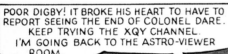

AS THE 'ASTRO-ARROW' ROCKETS EARTHWARDS THROUGH SPACE, SPACEMAN ALBERT FITZWILLIAM DIGBY AND JUNIOR CADET "FLAMER" SPRY ARE DEEP IN THE DEEPEST GLOOM.

SEEING COLONEL DARE B-BLOWN TO ATOMS LIKE THAT MADE ME *SICK*, SIR.

ME TOO, FLAMER — *AND DON'T "SIR" ME!*

SOME DAY — *SOMEHOW* — I'M GOING TO PAY OFF THAT GREEN DEVIL, THE MEKON, FOR WHAT HE DID TO MY COLONEL!

I'LL HAVE ANOTHER SHOT AT PICKING UP SOMETHING ON THE XQY SOUND AND VISION CHANNELS.

YOU'LL GET NOTHING BUT THE MEKON, LAD. HE'S PUT PAID TO OUR PALS — ALL THREE OF 'EM.

BUT DIGBY IS DUE FOR A SHOCK!

XQY CALLING EARTH H.Q.!

HEAVENLY BODIES!

"XQY CALLING EARTH H.Q.!"

GREAT GUNS!

JUMPING JETS!

DAN DARE'S DRAMATIC CALL WINGS THROUGH SPACE AND FALLS ON THE ASTONISHED EARS OF LISTENERS IN THE 'ASTRO-ARROW' AND AT EARTH HEAD-QUARTERS.

"XQY CALLING EARTH H.Q.!"

DAN HAS CONTACTED EARTH — BUT FLAMER AND STEVE ARE STILL IN THE MEKON'S HANDS. CAN DAN SAVE THEM AND HIMSELF? DON'T MISS NEXT WEEK'S EXCITING INSTALMENT!

FOURPENCE-HALFPENNY

EVERY WEDNESDAY

EAGLE

29 OCTOBER 1954 Vol. 5 No. 44

DAN DARE
PILOT OF THE FUTURE
PRISONERS OF SPACE

DAN DARE CALLING!

THE STORY SO FAR:
Believing that Dan Dare met his doom when the 'Performing Flea' was destroyed by the Treen flagship, the Mekon imprisons Steve Valiant and old Groupie in a "solar-cell" and prepares to launch them into space from space station XQY. The mechanism of the solar-cell is so contrived that the transparent sphere will circle Earth perpetually. Within the cell, Earth atmosphere is ensured for *twelve hours only!* Dan Dare, who baled out from the 'Flea's' escape hatch in his rocket-powered space-suit, succeeds in re-entering XQY. Having discovered the Mekon's grisly plot, Dan immediately contacts Hank, at Space H.Q. on Earth, by T-viewer.

...CALLING EARTH H.Q.!

VENERABLE VENUS! IT CAN'T BE!

ON XQY – THE LANDING BAY.

GO TO THE TURRET AND ESTABLISH CONTACT WITH EARTH! I WISH TO SPEAK TO SIR HUBERT GUEST...

...IT WILL BE INTERESTING TO SEE HIS REACTION TO THE NEWS OF DARE'S DEATH!

AT SPACE FLEET H.Q.

DAN! BY ALL THAT'S IMPOSSIBLE! HOW...?

CUT THE QUESTIONS, HANK, AND GET THE CONTROLLER– *TOUT DE SUITE!*

!

WHAT ON EARTH DOES *THAT* SIGNAL MEAN?

POOR DEEG! DAN'S DEATH HAS TURNED HIS BRAIN!

ACCORDING TO THE UNIVERSAL SPACE CODE, DIGBY IS "OUT OF CONTROL", "HOMEWARD BOUND", "ON FIRE", "*OUTWARD* BOUND", AND "WISHING ALL A MERRY XMAS"!

...AND A MOMENT LATER, HANK BURSTS HEADLONG INTO THE VIEWING ROOM.

YIPPEE! WHERE'S OLD HUBERT?

TIENS! *ANOTHER* MADMAN!

WHAT IS THE MEANING OF THIS LUNATIC INTRUSION?

YOU SEEM TO HAVE FORGOTTEN VERY QUICKLY THE PASSING OF A GALLANT COMRADE.

BUT HE *HASN'T* PASSED, SIR. I MEAN, HE'S ON THE T-VIEWER FROM XQY *RIGHT NOW!*

YOU MEAN...

COLONEL DARE'S...

STILL ALIVE?

THIS EXPLAINS DIGBY'S FIREWORK DISPLAY JUST NOW!

A FEW MOMENTS LATER...

DAN — MY BOY! HOW DID...?

NO TIME TO EXPLAIN! I'M ONLY HALF-A-JUMP AHEAD OF THE MEKON. HERE'S THE PLAN...

...SEND CRACK SQUADRON TO XQY *NOW!* I DON'T CARE IF THEY BURN THEMSELVES OUT GETTING HERE — BUT THEY *MUST ARRIVE* WITHIN TWELVE HOURS!

WHEN YOU ARRIVE, WATCH OUT FOR...

BUT, AS DAN UNFOLDS HIS PLAN, A GRIM GREEN GUN-MAN PREPARES FOR ACTION. *IT IS THE GUARD SENT BY THE MEKON TO CONTACT EARTH!* WILL DAN'S PLAN SUCCEED? READ NEXT WEEK'S EXCITING EPISODE!

FOURPENCE-HALFPENNY

EVERY WEDNESDAY

EAGLE

5 NOVEMBER 1954 Vol. 5 No. 45

DAN DARE
PILOT OF THE FUTURE
PRISONERS OF SPACE

ANOTHER EARTHMAN FOR MY MASTER'S SPORT!

THE STORY SO FAR: Believing that Dan Dare met his doom when the 'Performing Flea' was destroyed by the Treen flag-ship, the Mekon imprisons Steve Valiant and old Groupie in a "solar-cell" and prepares to launch them into space from space station XQY. The "solar-cell" contains Earth atmosphere for *twelve hours only!* Dan Dare, who baled out from the 'Flea' in his rocket-powered space-suit, re-enters XQY, discovers the Mekon's plot, hurries to the observation turret and contacts Sir Hubert Guest, on Earth, by T-viewer. Meanwhile, the Mekon sends his Chief Guard to the turret to get in touch with Earth, so that he can enjoy breaking the news of Dan's 'death' to Sir Hubert. The Guard arrives to find Dan bending over the T-viewer.

DAN!

WATCH OUT FOR MY PERSONAL IDENTIFICATION FLARES...

RAISE YOUR HANDS AND TURN 'ROUND!

DAN DARE, AT YOUR SERVICE!

THE EARTHMAN DARE! IT *CANNOT* BE! WE SAW YOU DIE!

SO WHAT? I HADN'T SQUARED ACCOUNTS WITH YOUR MISERABLE MASTER — SO I'VE COME BACK TO DO IT!

SEEING SUPERSTITION AND FEAR FLARE IN THE EYES OF THE TREEN GUARD, DAN PLAYS THE ROLL OF "GHOST" FOR ALL HE'S WORTH!

WE SAW THE "OLD ONE" DIE BY RAY-GUN, BUT HE, ALSO, IS STILL ALIVE! IF EARTHMEN HAVE CONQUERED DEATH, THE MEKON IS DOOMED.

THE MEKON'S DOOMED ALL RIGHT, MY FRIEND — BUT I MIGHT CONSIDER SPARING *YOUR* WORTHLESS HIDE — IF YOU'LL CO-OPERATE.

I SWEAR I WILL DO ANYTHING YOU ASK, O EARTHMAN, IF YOU WILL REVEAL TO ME THE SECRET BY WHICH YOU DEFEAT EVEN *DEATH* !

CONVINCED THAT DAN AND GROUPIE HAVE RETURNED FROM THE DEAD BY SOME NEW AND SECRET EARTH-METHOD, THE CHIEF TREEN GUARD REALIZES THAT THE MEKON IS POWERLESS AGAINST SUCH "SUPERMEN". IN RETURN FOR DAN'S PROMISE TO REVEAL HIS "SECRET OF SURVIVAL", THE GUARD SWEARS TO OBEY HIM TO THE LAST.

"DEATH-DEFYING DARE!" H'M! IF I TOLD HIM THE TRUTH — THAT I ESCAPED BY SHEER LUCK — HE'D SING A DIFFERENT TUNE. I GUESS I'D BETTER STRING THIS TREEN ALONG.

BEFORE I ACCEPT YOUR ALLEGIANCE, YOU MUST SWEAR BY THE GREAT LORD DIGGERTY-DOO, FITZY-BITZY-WILLIAMBUS THAT YOU WILL OBEY ME IN ALL THINGS.

BY THE GREAT LORD DIGGERTY-DOO, FITZY-BITZY-WILLIAMBUS, I SWEAR!

WHEN MY MISSION IS ACCOMPLISHED, I SHALL TELL YOU THE SECRET OF MY SURVIVAL.

AND WON'T YOU BE SURPRISED, YOU GREEN GUMP!

THE MEKON SENT ME TO COMMUNICATE WITH THE CONTROLLER ON EARTH. HE WISHES TO TELL SIR HUBERT GUEST OF YOUR DEATH.

SIR HUBERT! HE MUST BE FAIRLY SIZZLING ON THAT SCREEN BY NOW!

THANK HEAVEN!

DANNY-BOY! WHAT HAPPENED?

THE DRILL FIRST — THE CASE-HISTORY LATER — IF I GET OUT OF THIS!

ELITE SQUADRON IS WAITING TO SCRAMBLE. I'M LEADING THE SORTIE MYSELF. COMPLETE YOUR ORDERS FOR ACTION, COLONEL DARE!

PROCEED HERE AT MAXIMUM POWER! CRUISE OUT OF RANGE OF XQY'S SPACE-GUNS! IF MY LUCK HOLDS, I'LL BE FLYING FREE IN THE AREA IN SPACE-SUIT. WATCH FOR MY PERSONAL FLARE-IDENTIFICATION!

EARTHMAN!

THE MEKON COMETH!

WHERE IS THE FOOL I SENT TO CONTACT EARTH?

WILL DAN'S NEW ALLY REMAIN STEADFAST? WATCH FOR NEXT WEEK'S EXCITING DEVELOPMENTS!

FOURPENCE-HALFPENNY

EVERY WEDNESDAY

EAGLE

12 NOVEMBER 1954 Vol. 5 No. 46

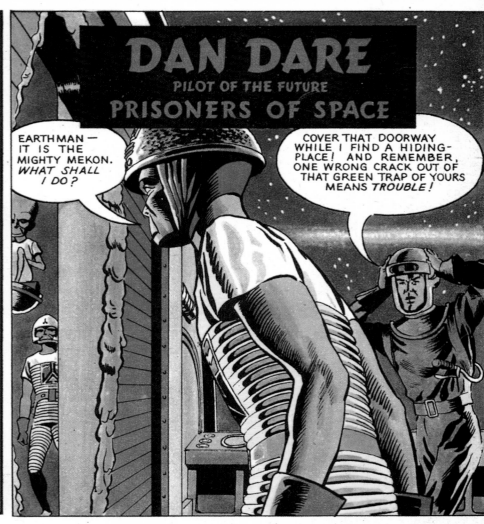

DAN DARE
PILOT OF THE FUTURE
PRISONERS OF SPACE

EARTHMAN — IT IS THE MIGHTY MEKON. *WHAT SHALL I DO?*

COVER THAT DOORWAY WHILE I FIND A HIDING-PLACE! AND REMEMBER, ONE WRONG CRACK OUT OF THAT GREEN TRAP OF YOURS MEANS *TROUBLE!*

THE STORY SO FAR:
Sent by the Mekon to contact Sir Hubert Guest, at Earth H.Q., a Chief Treen Guard reaches the observation turret on space station XQY and finds Dan Dare already at the T-viewer. The Guard, having seen the complete destruction of the 'Performing Flea' by the rebel Treen flagship, believes that Dan has returned from the dead. Terrified, he swears to obey Dan in all things. At that moment, the ruthless Mekon and his guards approach the shattered door of the observation turret. As Dan dives for cover, he hisses one last warning to Sir Hubert Guest, who is still in T-viewer contact with XQY.

'WARE MEKON, CHIEF! STICK TO MY PLAN AND BLUFF HIS GREEN LUGS OFF!

WHAT ON EARTH GOES *ON* UP THERE, HANK?

YOUR GUESS IS AS GOOD AS MINE, SIR — BUT I'LL BET MARS TO A BLOOD-ORANGE, DAN'S GOT IT UNDER CONTROL.

I HAVE ESTABLISHED COMMUNICATION WITH EARTH H.Q., O MASTER! THE CONTROLLER AWAITS YOUR EXALTED PRESENCE.

WHY DO YOU TREMBLE, FOOL?

I AM TROUBLED, O MIGHTY ONE! WE DESTROY THESE EARTHMEN, *AND YET THEY STILL LIVE!*

THIS IS IT! HE'S GOING TO SPILL THE BEANS ABOUT ME STILL BEING IN PLAY.

WHAT DO YOU MEAN?

SPEAK — OR I SHALL GIVE THE WORD WHICH WILL SILENCE YOUR FOOLISH TONGUE FOREVER!

IT IS THE TRUTH, MASTER! THESE EARTHMEN *CANNOT* BE KILLED. I HAVE SEEN LIVING PROOF OF THAT!

THE CHIEF GUARD'S BRAIN, LONG CONDITIONED TO INSTANT OBEDIENCE, IS TORN BETWEEN TWO FEARS . . .

IF I BETRAY THE EARTHMAN DARE, THE MEKON WILL SURELY REWARD ME AND DESTROY DARE . . .

. . . BUT AS DARE DEFIES DEATH, *HE MAY COME BACK A SECOND TIME AND DESTROY ME!*

I WISH I KNEW WHAT'S GOING ON IN HIS GREEN BEAN. *WHY DOESN'T HE SPEAK?*

THE OLD ONE CALLED "GROUPIE" STILL LIVES, ALTHOUGH HE RECEIVED THE FULL BLAST OF A RAY-GUN AT SHORT RANGE, O MASTER — THAT WAS MY MEANING.

THE WEAPON WAS FAULTY. THERE CAN BE NO OTHER EXPLANATION.

CRAVEN FOOL! ONE SUCH AS YOU COULD EVEN BELIEVE DARE ESCAPED UTTER DESTRUCTION WHEN HIS SHIP BLEW UP BEFORE OUR VERY EYES.

PHEW! THAT WAS CLOSE!

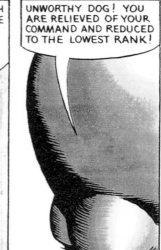

UNWORTHY DOG! YOU ARE RELIEVED OF YOUR COMMAND AND REDUCED TO THE LOWEST RANK!

AS THE TENSION MOMENTARILY EASES FOR DAN DARE, THE MEKON TURNS TO THE T-VIEWER . . .

STRANGE — I FEEL REMARKABLY *ALIVE!*

IT IS MY PLEASURE, SIR HUBERT, TO INFORM YOU THAT *COLONEL DAN DARE IS DEAD!*

ALTHOUGH THAT FAT AND STUPID SPACEMAN "DIGBY" AND THE YOUNG EARTH-CHILD WITH THE RED HAIR ESCAPED ME, I STILL HOLD THE BOY CALLED "VALIANT" AND THE ANCIENT ONE KNOWN AS "GROUPIE".

FOLLOWING DAN'S ORDERS, SIR HUBERT PLAYS A GAME OF BLUFF . . .

ALL RIGHT! YOU'VE SETTLED YOUR SCORE WITH DARE FOR ALL TIME AND YOU HOLD TWO EARTH HOSTAGES. *WHAT ARE YOUR TERMS FOR RELEASING THEM?*

WITHDRAW YOUR OCCUPATION FORCES FROM VENUS, SO THAT I CAN RETURN AND REBUILD THE GREAT CITY OF MEKONTA AND THUS RULE AGAIN UPON MY OWN PLANET.

ONLY EARTH GOVERNMENT CAN AGREE TO SUCH TERMS.

THEN CALL YOUR PUNY STATESMEN TOGETHER. TELL THEM THEY MUST DECIDE BEFORE THE FIRST RAY OF THE SUN TOUCHES THIS SATELLITE.

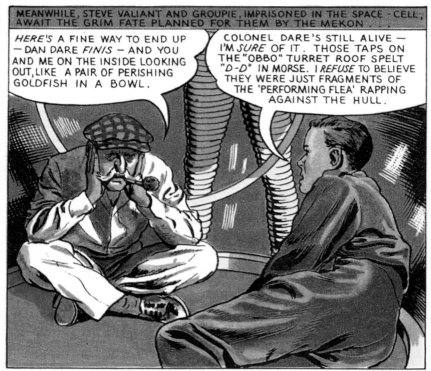

MEANWHILE, STEVE VALIANT AND GROUPIE, IMPRISONED IN THE SPACE-CELL, AWAIT THE GRIM FATE PLANNED FOR THEM BY THE MEKON . . .

HERE'S A FINE WAY TO END UP — DAN DARE *FINIS* — AND YOU AND ME ON THE INSIDE LOOKING OUT, LIKE A PAIR OF PERISHING GOLDFISH IN A BOWL.

COLONEL DARE'S STILL ALIVE — I'M *SURE* OF IT. THOSE TAPS ON THE "OBBO" TURRET ROOF SPELT "D-D" IN MORSE. *I REFUSE* TO BELIEVE THEY WERE JUST FRAGMENTS OF THE 'PERFORMING FLEA' RAPPING AGAINST THE HULL.

. . . AND DAN AWAITS HIS CHANCE . . .

TILL SUNRISE! IF THE CRACK EARTH SQUADRONS ARE SCRAMBLING EVEN *NOW*, THEY'LL BARELY MAKE IT!

CAN DAN PLAN A WAY OF SAVING STEVE AND GROUPIE? WATCH FOR NEXT WEEK'S EXCITING INSTALMENT!

FOURPENCE-HALFPENNY

EVERY WEDNESDAY

EAGLE

COMPANION TO GIRL, SWIFT AND ROBIN

19 NOVEMBER 1954 Vol. 5 No. 47

DAN DARE
PILOT OF THE FUTURE
PRISONERS OF SPACE

...PROCEEDING IN SPEARHEAD FORMATION WITH MYSELF LEADING IN 'SPEEDSTAR'. WE HAVE ONE OBJECTIVE — TO REACH XQY *WITHIN TWELVE HOURS!* FROM THEN ON, WE SHALL BE IN THE CAPABLE HANDS OF COLONEL DARE. NO DOUBT HE WILL FIND SOME MEANS OF CONTACTING US WITH DETAILS OF HIS ACTION PLAN.

THE STORY SO FAR:
Believing that Dan Dare perished in the 'Performing Flea', when it was destroyed by the Treen flagship, the Mekon contacts Sir Hubert Guest, at Earth H.Q., on the T-viewer. He offers to release Senior Cadet Steve Valiant and old Groupie if all Earth occupation forces are withdrawn immediately from Venus, thus enabling him to rebuild the city of Mekonta and re-enslave the free Treens and Therons. Dan, having bluffed the Mekon's Chief Guard into believing he has returned from the dead, has already told Sir Hubert Guest to send Spacefleet's crack squadron to space station XQY. While waiting for help to arrive, Dan plays a perilous game of hide-and-seek on the vast, man-made satellite, where Steve and Groupie are imprisoned in a solar-cell which will contain Earth atmosphere for *twelve hours only!* Meanwhile, on Earth, Sir Hubert gives his final briefing.

ONE LAST WORD, MEN! THIS IS A BLIND OPERATION. WE RELY UPON DARE'S BARE WORD THAT WE ARE URGENTLY NEEDED AT XQY. THAT IS GOOD ENOUGH FOR *ME* — AND I'M SURE IT'S GOOD ENOUGH FOR *YOU.* THAT IS ALL!

HERE ARE PLOTTING ROOM DETAILS OF THE 'ASTRO-ARROW'S' HOMEWARD COURSE. AT THE POINT INDICATED, YOU WILL BREAK FORMATION AND ESCORT HER BACK TO EARTH.

HAVE A HEART, CHIEF! DANNY'S OUR BEST PAL!

YOU MAKE THE JOKE, SIR HUBERT?

AS THE CRACK SQUADRON 'SCRAMBLES', SIR HUBERT ISSUES FINAL ORDERS TO DAN'S CLOSEST FRIENDS.

IT'S NO JOKE, PIERRE! ALTHOUGH NOTHING'S SHOWN UP ON THE RADAR SCREEN SO FAR, IT'S QUITE POSSIBLE THE MEKON'S GOT ONE OF HIS SHIPS TAILING THE 'ASTRO-ARROW'. IF SO, YOU'LL GET *MORE* THAN YOUR SHARE OF ACTION! TAKE YOUR STATIONS!

PLUS NINETEEN! PLUS EIGHTEEN! PLUS SEVENTEEN!

LAFAYETTE AND HOGAN — "UNIVERSAL NURSEMAIDS". *BAH!*

THE HISTORY BOOKS TELL OF ONE, LORD NELSON, WHO TURNED A BLIND EYE TO AN ORDER HE DID NOT WISH TO SEE...

PLUS ELEVEN! PLUS TEN!

PERHAPS *WE* WILL TAKE A LEAF FROM THAT BOOK, MON AMI! *STAND BY FOR TAKE-OFF!*

TEN SECONDS LATER, THE EARTH SQUADRON ROCKETS TOWARDS ITS 'BLIND DATE' IN SPACE WITH DAN DARE!

FOURPENCE-HALFPENNY

EVERY WEDNESDAY

EAGLE

COMPANION TO GIRL, SWIFT AND ROBIN

26 NOVEMBER 1954 Vol. 5 No. 48

DAN DARE
PILOT OF THE FUTURE
PRISONERS OF SPACE

SPACEFLEET'S "ELITE" SQUADRON! THERE'S A SIGHT TO SHAKE THAT MILDEWED MONSTROSITY THE MEKON! BUT HE'S NOT GOING TO SEE IT — YET! STAND CLEAR!

EVEN IF YOU DESTROY ALL METHODS OF COMMUNICATION HERE, EARTHMAN, THE MEKON STILL HAS SIMILAR EQUIPMENT IN HIS FLAGSHIP.

THE STORY SO FAR:
Believing that Dan Dare died in the wreckage of the 'Performing Flea', the ruthless Mekon communicates with Sir Hubert Guest, at Earth H.Q., and offers to release his hostages, Steve Valiant and old Groupie, if all Earth forces are withdrawn from Venus so that he can re-impose his tyrannical rule over the inhabitants. Aware that Dan Dare is still very much alive, Sir Hubert Guest, Spacefleet's Controller, is leading his crack squadron towards space station XQY, where Dan has enlisted the aid of the Mekon's discredited Chief Guard. As the Mekon leaves the observation turret of the vast, man-made satellite, Dan begins his task of wrecking all radar and viewing equipment.

THEN WE'LL FIND SOME WAY OF SABOTAGING THAT LOT, TOO! WHAT ARE YOU CALLED?

I AM "XALTO", WHICH MEANS RISING SUN. BUT UNLESS YOU TELL ME YOUR SECRET OF LIFE-OVER-DEATH, I FEAR I SHALL NEVER LIVE TO SEE ANOTHER SUNRISE.

A FEW MINUTES LATER, DAN DARE SURVEYS HIS VIOLENT HANDIWORK WITH SATISFACTION.

THE BEST BOFFIN-BRAINS IN THE UNIVERSE COULDN'T PUT THIS MESS RIGHT INSIDE TWELVE HOURS...

...AND BY THAT TIME, OUR TROUBLES WILL BE OVER, XALTO — ONE WAY OR ANOTHER!

A TWELVE-SECOND BURST OF PARALYZING GAS WILL KEEP THIS BABY UNDER FOR AS MANY HOURS. TAKE HIS HELMET, XALTO!

HOW CAN YOU MAKE PLANS SO SWIFTLY? ALL OURS ARE WORKED OUT IN THE MIGHTY MEKON'S MIND. WITHOUT HIM, WE CANNOT ACT.

FORGET THAT MELON-HEADED MONKEY! I'M GOING TO TEACH YOU THE ART OF IMPROVISATION, XALTO MY LAD!

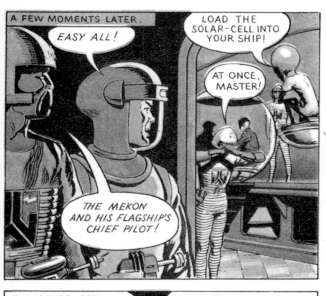

A FEW MOMENTS LATER.

EASY ALL!

LOAD THE SOLAR-CELL INTO YOUR SHIP!

AT ONCE, MASTER!

THE MEKON AND HIS FLAGSHIP'S CHIEF PILOT!

YOU WILL LAUNCH THE CELL INTO SPACE *ONE EARTH HOUR* FROM NOW!

THEN THE TWO EARTH HOSTAGES ARE TO DIE, O MIGHTY ONE?

NOT YET! THEY SHALL BE *PRISONERS OF SPACE* UNTIL SIR HUBERT GUEST ACCEPTS OR REJECTS MY TERMS!

BUT, XALTO — IF HE LAUNCHES THAT BEASTLY BUBBLE, HOW *THE DICKENS* DOES HE EXPECT TO RECOVER IT?

THE SOLAR-CELL MECHANISM SENDS OUT A CONSTANT SIGNAL WHICH REGISTERS ON THE AUDIO-PANEL OF HIS FLAGSHIP, O EARTHMAN!

THEN IT'S USELESS TO TRY TO DESTROY THE FLAGSHIP'S SOUND-AND-VISION SET-UP! WITHIN THE HOUR, THE MEKON'S BOUND TO SEND SOMEONE TO THE "OBBO" TURRET TO OPEN THE MAIN AIR-LOCK DOOR—HE'LL FIND THAT PARALYZED GUARD AND THE WRECKED ASTROSCOPE ...OH, MY STARS!

HELPLESS PAWNS IN THE CENTRE OF THIS GRIM GAME, STEVE VALIANT AND OLD GROUPIE "SIT IT OUT" IN THE SOLAR-CELL. MEANWHILE, COUNTLESS MILES AWAY, THE 'ASTRO-ARROW' PREPARES TO RENDEZVOUS WITH 'LODESTAR'. PILOTED BY PIERRE AND NAVIGATED BY HANK.

WE'LL SPIN IN SPACE LIKE A TINY MOON — A PERPETUAL WARNING TO FUTURE GENERATIONS TO KEEP THEIR TWO BLINKING FEET ON THE GROUND, STEVE!

IT'LL TAKE MORE THAN THAT TO KEEP LADS LIKE YOUNG FLAMER SPRY OUT OF SPACEFLEET, GROUPIE. I WONDER IF DIGBY AND FLAMER MADE A SAFE EARTH-FALL?

DEAD ON COURSE — AND NINETY SECONDS TO GO! STAND BY TO CUT POWER AND BLOW REACTORS!

ALL SET, FLAMER! GIVE ME THE COUNT!

ABOARD 'LODESTAR'

'ASTRO-ARROW' IN VISION, MAJOR LAFAYETTE!

58-57-56-55-54..!

ADVISE 'SPEEDSTAR' I AM BREAKING FORMATION!

AS ELITE SQUADRON SPEEDS ONWARD, 'LODESTAR' PEELS OFF TO MAKE A PERFECT RENDEZVOUS WITH THE 'ASTRO-ARROW'.

CUT POWER! BLOW REACTORS!

CUT POWER! BLOW REACTORS!

MAGNETIC GRAPPLING DEVICES BRING THE SHIPS ALONGSIDE, THE COMMUNICATION AIR-LOCKS ARE MADE FAST, AND A FEW MINUTES LATER THE TWO CREWS MEET IN THE 'LODESTAR'.

DEEG!

PIERRE!

WELCOME ABOARD, MY YOUNG HERO!

THANKS, SIR!

BACK TO THE 'ASTRO-ARROW', PRONTO, YOU TWO!

MY CO-PILOT WILL TAKE YOU SAFELY TO EARTH. WE'RE GOING ON TO XQY!

GREAT MINDS THINK ALIKE, MAJOR! I HAD THE SAME IDEA.

YOU BET! *WE'RE* COMING WITH YOU, SIR!

CRAZY! LOOPY! NUTS!

IMPOSSIBLE! RIDICULOUS! ABSURD!

WILL DIGBY AND FLAMER PERSUADE PIERRE AND HANK TO AGREE TO THEIR RECKLESS PLAN? AND WHAT OF DAN DARE — FACED WITH THE PROBLEM OF KNOWING THAT SOON THE MEKON WILL LEARN OF THE PRESENCE OF AN ENEMY STILL ACTIVE ON XQY? WATCH FOR NEXT WEEK'S EXCITING DEVELOPMENTS!

FOURPENCE-HALFPENNY

EVERY WEDNESDAY

EAGLE

COMPANION TO GIRL, SWIFT AND ROBIN

3 DECEMBER 1954 Vol. 5 No. 49

DAN DARE
PILOT OF THE FUTURE
PRISONERS OF SPACE

HAVE A HEART, HANK! YOU *CAN'T* LEAVE US OUT OF THIS SHOW.

I STARTED THIS WHOLE SHOOTING MATCH, MAJOR LAFAYETTE — *PLEASE* LET ME BE IN AT THE FINISH!

IT'S *HAYWIRE*, BUT . . .

IT'S *FANTASTIQUE*, BUT . . .

THE STORY SO FAR: Believing that Dan Dare is dead, the Mekon gets in touch with Sir Hubert Guest, at Earth H.Q., and offers to release his hostages, Steve and Groupie, if all Earth forces are withdrawn from Venus so that he can re-impose his tyrannical rule over the inhabitants. Aware that Dan is still very much alive, Sir Hubert is leading his crack squadron towards space station XQY, where Dan has enlisted the aid of the Mekon's discredited Chief Guard, Xalto. As the elite squadron speeds to the rescue, the spaceship 'Lodestar' peels off to rendezvous with the 'Astro-Arrow' and escort her back to Earth. Hank and Pierre are shaken rigid at Digby's suggestion that he and young Flamer Spry should tranship to 'Lodestar', leaving Pierre's co-pilot to take the 'Astro-Arrow' back to base.

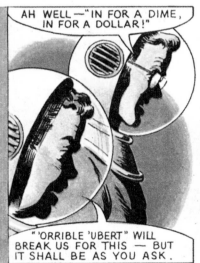

AH WELL —"IN FOR A DIME, IN FOR A DOLLAR!"

"'ORRIBLE 'UBERT" WILL BREAK US FOR THIS — BUT IT SHALL BE AS YOU ASK.

WE'RE *IN*, YOUNG 'UN!

WHAT A BREAK!

BON VOYAGE, MON AMI!

I'LL MAKE IT ALL RIGHT, SIR!

I CAN SEE IT IN THE SPACE GAZETTE NOW —"CAPTAIN HOGAN REDUCED TO RANKS FOR IRRESPONSIBILITY!"

A FEW MINUTES LATER, THE TWO SPACE-SHIPS TEAR OFF IN OPPOSITE DIRECTIONS — ONE EARTHWARDS, THE OTHER IN THE WAKE OF ELITE SQUADRON.

THIS MISSION SHOULD TAKE LITTLE TIME. I SHALL ACCOMPANY YOU!

I AM HONOURED, O MIGHTY ONE!

MEANWHILE, ON SPACE STATION XQY, THE SOLAR-CELL CONTAINING STEVE AND GROUPIE IS LOADED INTO THE MEKON'S FLAGSHIP.

SEND A GUARD TO OPEN THE MAIN AIR-LOCKS AND TO CHECK ANY ACTIVITY IN EARTH ORBIT!

DAN DARE AND XALTO OVERHEAR THE MEKON'S ORDER FROM THEIR HIDING PLACE.

THIS IS THE END, EARTHMAN! THE MIGHTY MEKON WILL LEARN WHAT HAS HAPPENED IN THE TURRET!

NOT IF I KNOW IT, PAL! *COME ON!*

A FEW MOMENTS LATER, THE MEKON'S MESSENGER ENTERS THE OBSERVATION TURRET.

THANK GOODNESS I DIDN'T BUST THE INTERCOM WHEN I SMASHED THE VIEWING GEAR. *NOW FOR IT!*

THAT'S SETTLED *HIS* HASH FOR THE TIME BEING. OUR BAG'S GROWING FAST, XALTO! GET ON TO THAT INTERCOM—LIVELY!

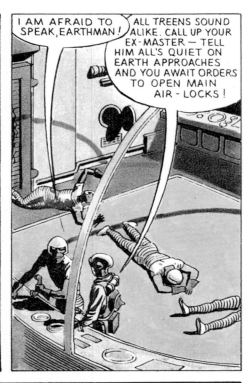

I AM AFRAID TO SPEAK, EARTHMAN!

ALL TREENS SOUND ALIKE. CALL UP YOUR EX-MASTER — TELL HIM ALL'S QUIET ON EARTH APPROACHES AND YOU AWAIT ORDERS TO OPEN MAIN AIR-LOCKS!

ALL IS WELL, MASTER! I AWAIT YOUR ORDERS.

GIVE THE COUNT IN EARTH-UNITS — WE ARE READY FOR LAUNCHING!

WHERE DO YOU GO, O EARTHMAN?

OUT! IF THE FLAG-SHIP'S ONLY GOING TO DROP THE SOLAR-CELL, SHE WON'T USE JETS —SHE'LL PROCEED UNDER LOW POWER AND RETURN AT ONCE. SHE'S GOING TO CARRY SUPER-CARGO — *ME!*

A FEW MINUTES LATER, THE TREEN FLAGSHIP SLOWLY EMERGES FROM THE OPEN AIR-LOCK DOOR OF BAY NUMBER ONE.

DEAD LUCKY I GUESSED RIGHT! IF HE'D USED JETS FOR TAKE-OFF, I'D HAVE BEEN UNLUCKY—AND *DEAD!*

THIS IS *IT*, STEVE!

CHIN UP, GROUPIE!

THERE THEY SHALL STAY, PRISONERS OF SPACE, UNTIL EARTH ACCEPTS MY TERMS — OR FOR ALL ETERNITY!

YOU CAN SCRUB OUT ANY IDEA OF DAN DARE RESCUING US NOW, STEVE. HE'S A GONER— SAME AS *WE'LL* BE!

JUMPING JETS, GROUPIE! *WHAT'S THAT ON THE NACELLE OF THE TREEN SHIP?*

WILL DAN DARE'S DESPERATE GAMBLE COME OFF? AND HOW CAN HE HOPE TO SAVE STEVE AND GROUPIE? WATCH FOR NEXT WEEK'S EXCITING INSTALMENT!

FOURPENCE-HALFPENNY

EVERY WEDNESDAY

EAGLE

COMPANION TO GIRL, SWIFT AND ROBIN

10 DECEMBER 1954 Vol. 5 No. 50

THE STORY SO FAR:
The ruthless Mekon, in a bid to regain power over the inhabitants of Venus, orders the rebel Treen flagship to launch the solar-cell, containing Steve Valiant and old Groupie, into space. Knowing that Spacefleet's Elite squadron from Earth, led by Sir Hubert Guest, cannot reach space station XQY for some time, Dan Dare, with no motive power beyond the tiny jet motor of his spacesuit, attaches himself to a nacelle of the flagship, in a desperate gamble to rescue his pals from the limitless void of space.

FOURPENCE-HALFPENNY

EVERY WEDNESDAY

EAGLE

COMPANION TO GIRL, SWIFT AND ROBIN

17 DECEMBER 1954 Vol. 5 No. 51

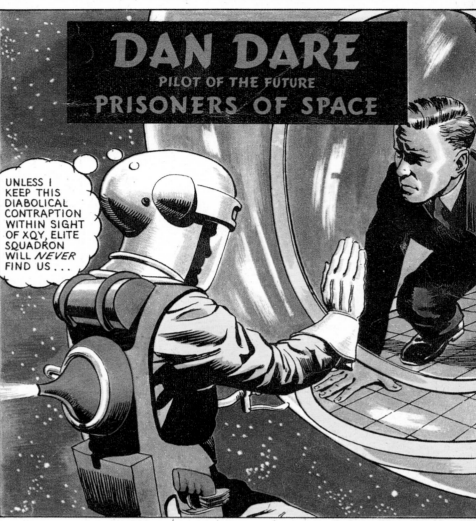

DAN DARE
PILOT OF THE FUTURE
PRISONERS OF SPACE

UNLESS I KEEP THIS DIABOLICAL CONTRAPTION WITHIN SIGHT OF XQY, ELITE SQUADRON WILL *NEVER* FIND US . . .

THE STORY SO FAR: The ruthless Mekon, who believes Dan Dare is dead, launches the solar-cell containing his hostages, Steve Valiant and Groupie, into space, hoping that Earth will agree to his sinister terms in order to save them. Whilst waiting for Elite squadron, commanded by Sir Hubert Guest, to arrive from Earth, Dan Dare leaves Xalto, his Treen ally and formerly the Mekon's Chief Guard, in space station XQY and uses the power of his tiny rocket motor to guide the solar-cell off its course and keep it circling XQY.

. . . AND YET, IF I STAY ON THIS NEW ORBIT, SOONER OR LATER THE MEKON'S *BOUND* TO REALIZE SOMEONE'S TAMPERING WITH THIS BLOOMING BUBBLE.

WITHOUT A CLUE, DAN DECIDES TO CHANCE OPERATING THE EXTERNAL CONTROLS OF THE SOLAR-CELL IN THE HOPE OF CREATING A BLACKOUT.

THREE SWITCHES — IF I THROW THE WRONG ONE, IT MAY CUT OUT THE PRESSURIZING DEVICE AND PUT-PAID TO STEVE AND GROUPIE . . .

. . . BUT I'VE *GOT* TO RISK IT!

PHEW! MY LUCK HOLDS! THAT SWITCH HAS CUT THE JETS AS WELL AS THE LIGHTS. NOW BACK TO BASE!

A FEW MOMENTS LATER.

SAFE — FOR THE TIME BEING . . .

. . . BUT I'LL BET THERE'S A FULL FLAP ON INSIDE. I WONDER HOW POOR OLD XALTO'S FARING UP THERE ?

FOURPENCE-HALFPENNY

EVERY WEDNESDAY

EAGLE

COMPANION TO GIRL, SWIFT AND ROBIN

24 DECEMBER 1954 Vol. 5 No. 52

DAN DARE
PILOT OF THE FUTURE
PRISONERS OF SPACE

IT IS IMPOSSIBLE FOR THE SOLAR-CELL TO HAVE TRAVELLED BEYOND THE RANGE OF OUR INSTRUMENTS IN SO SHORT A TIME. THE ANSWER IS CLEAR — IT IS NOT TOO FAR AWAY TO REGISTER UPON OUR SCREENS — *BUT TOO CLOSE!*

BEWARE, O MEKON! IF THE EARTHMAN DARE IS SO NEAR, *THEN SO IS YOUR END!*

THE STORY SO FAR:
Due to the accidental take-off of the 'Performing Flea', Groupie, Flamer Spry and Steve Valiant reach space station XQY, which the Mekon and his rebel Treens have captured. The Mekon offers to exchange his hostages for Dan Dare. So Dare sets off in the 'Astro-Arrow', accompanied by Digby, on what he believes is a flight to certain death. Later, Digby and Flamer escape in the 'Astro-Arrow'. Attempting to follow in the 'Flea', Dan damages her tail and loses control. The 'Flea' is destroyed by the Treen flagship. Certain that Dan is dead, the Mekon imprisons Steve and Groupie in a solar-cell and launches it into space. Dan, still very much alive, leaves Xalto, his Treen ally, in XQY and uses the motor of his space-suit to steer the cell back to the base of XQY. Meanwhile, the Mekon captures Xalto and discovers that the solar-cell is off course.

IF THE TRAITOR XALTO SPEAKS TRUTH AND DARE STILL LIVES, YOU WILL NOT HAVE FAR TO SEEK.

HE CAN DO LITTLE AGAINST SO MANY, MASTER!

THE AIR-LOCK MECHANISM'S IN OPERATION! I'D BETTER GO TOP-SIDE AND SEE WHAT DEVILISH DISH THE MEKON'S COOKING UP *THIS* TIME!

I GET IT, GROUPIE! DAN'S GOING UP TO RECONNOITRE!

THAT'S TORN IT!

... the Mekon sends out his squad, equipped with space-flares, to find the solar-cell.

THE MEKON'S FLYING SQUAD! *HE'S RUMBLED MY RUSE!*

THOSE SPACE-BORNE GRASSHOPPERS ARE *CERTAIN* TO FIND THE SOLAR-CELL, BUT WHILE I'M FREE, THERE'S *STILL* A CHANCE OF DIDDLING OLD MELON-HEAD.

BY THE LIGHT OF THEIR SPACE-FLARES, THE MEKON'S MINIONS SOON LOCATE THE SOLAR-CELL.

THEY'VE GOT US AGAIN, STEVE-BOY — AND IT'S ONLY A MATTER OF TIME BEFORE THEY GET DAN!

THEY HAVEN'T GOT HIM YET, GROUPIE — AND WHILE THERE'S LIFE, THERE'S HOPE!

LATER...

XALTO LIED, O MASTER. WE HAVE SEARCHED EVERY INCH OF THE OUTER HULL, BUT THERE IS NO SIGN OF THE EARTHMAN.

THEN WHOSE HAND TAMPERED WITH THE EXTERNAL SWITCHES OF THE SOLAR-CELL? BRING THE EARTHLINGS FORTH! I WILL QUESTION THEM.

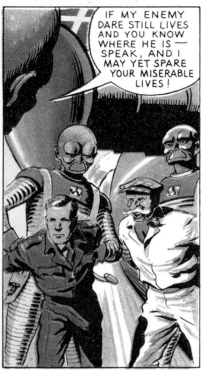

IF MY ENEMY DARE STILL LIVES AND YOU KNOW WHERE HE IS — SPEAK, AND I MAY YET SPARE YOUR MISERABLE LIVES!

YOU GHASTLY GHERKIN! EVEN IF WE KNEW, WE WOULDN'T TELL YOU!

WE DON'T BARGAIN WITH BRUTES. YOU'VE HAD A LONG RUN, MEKON, BUT YOU'RE NEAR THE END OF YOUR ROPE!

WE SHALL SEE! PREPARE FOR IMMEDIATE TAKE-OFF! OUR LAST TASK WILL BE TO DESTROY THIS SATELLITE UTTERLY. THEN, IF DARE *IS* IN FREE SPACE, TEN MILLION EARTHSHIPS WOULD HAVE NO CHANCE OF FINDING HIM!

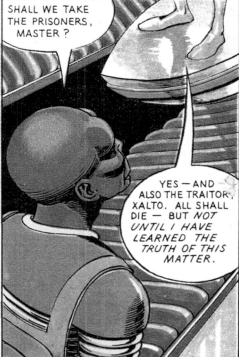

SHALL WE TAKE THE PRISONERS, MASTER?

YES — AND ALSO THE TRAITOR, XALTO. ALL SHALL DIE — BUT *NOT UNTIL I HAVE LEARNED THE TRUTH OF THIS MATTER.*

A FEW MOMENTS LATER, THE THREE TREEN SHIPS ARE READY FOR TAKE-OFF. INSIDE THE FLAGSHIP, THE MEKON GIVES HIS FINAL ORDERS.

BOTH OTHER SHIPS ARE MANNED, O MASTER, AND THE X BOMB IS PREPARED.

GOOD! OPEN THE BOMB DOORS!

AS THE DOORS BENEATH THE TREEN FLAG-SHIP OPEN TO DEPOSIT THE BOMB IN THE LANDING-DOCK OF XQY...

JUMPING JETS! *WHAT'S THIS?*

BOMB GONE — DARE IN!

...DAN RAPIDLY CLAMBERS ABOARD. WITH ELITE SQUADRON, RACING TO THE RESCUE FROM EARTH, STILL HOURS AWAY AND THE MEKON'S FLEET SETTING OUT FOR AN UNKNOWN DESTINATION, WHAT WILL BE DAN'S NEXT MOVE? WATCH FOR NEXT WEEK'S FAST-MOVING EPISODE

FOURPENCE-HALFPENNY

EVERY WEDNESDAY

EAGLE

COMPANION TO GIRL, SWIFT AND ROBIN

31 DECEMBER 1954 Vol. 5 No. 53

DAN DARE
PILOT OF THE FUTURE
PRISONERS OF SPACE

AS THE REBEL TREEN SHIPS ROCKET AWAY FROM SPACE STATION XQY...

...DAN DARE CROUCHES IN THE BOMB-BAY OF THE MEKON'S FLAGSHIP, WHICH IS SPEEDING TOWARDS AN UNKNOWN DESTINATION, CARRYING THE MEKON'S TWO EARTH HOSTAGES, STEVE VALIANT AND OLD GROUPIE. AWARE THAT A SQUADRON FROM EARTH IS ON THE WAY TO XQY, THE MEKON HAS SET A TIME-BOMB IN THE VAST SATELLITE.

FOR ONE BRIEF MOMENT, THE DARKNESS OF OUTER SPACE IS ILLUMINATED BY A BLINDING WHITE FLASH, AS XQY DISINTEGRATES INTO A CLOUD OF ATOMIC DUST.

PHEW! THAT'LL BE THE ATOMIC EGG I CHANGED PLACES WITH!

EARTH FOOLS! SEE HOW EASILY THEIR FLIMSY OUTPOSTS IN SPACE ARE DESTROYED!

WHAT COURSE SHALL I SET, O MASTER?

TO VENUS—AND THE RUINS OF MEKONTA! NOW DARE IS DEAD BEYOND ALL DOUBT, I SHALL RALLY THE TREEN POPULATION TO MY CAUSE AGAIN!

MEANWHILE, IN 'SPEEDSTAR', THE LEADING SHIP OF ELITE SQUADRON

I HAD XQY IN PERFECT VISION FIVE SECONDS AGO, SIR. THERE WAS A BRIEF FLASH AND NOW SHE'S VANISHED COMPLETELY.

THAT'S BAD! COLONEL DARE REPORTED THREE TREEN SHIPS LYING BEHIND HER. EXTEND YOUR RANGE AND TRY TO PICK THEM UP!

A SQUADRON IS ONLY AS FAST AS ITS SLOWEST SHIP, SIR HUBERT. ONLY 'SPEEDSTAR' AND 'LODESTAR' COULD HOPE TO OUTSTRIP THE MEKON'S FLEET.

AND I SENT 'LODESTAR' TO ESCORT THE 'ASTRO-ARROW' BACK TO EARTH! IT LOOKS AS IF WE MAY HAVE TO GO IT ALONE, SONDAR, AND LEAVE THE REST OF ELITE TO FOLLOW AT THE BEST SPEED THEY CAN MAKE.

A FEW MINUTES LATER.

I'VE LOCATED 'EM, SIR! LINE ABREAST — AND THEY APPEAR TO BE ON COURSE TO VENUS!

ALERT THERON H.Q. ON VENUS IMMEDIATELY! THEN INSTRUCT ALL ELITE COMMANDERS TO STAND BY FOR CHANGE OF PLANS.

'SPEEDSTAR' WILL PROCEED AT MAXIMUM POWER!

YOU WILL FOLLOW IN FORMATION AT TOP SPEED!

ALL RIGHT, CAPTAIN! LET'S HAVE THE BEST SHE CAN GIVE US!

WAIT, SIR! WE'VE JUST HAD A SIGNAL FROM 'LODESTAR'.

'LODESTAR'? IMPOSSIBLE! SHE'S BACK AT H.Q. BY NOW!

NO, SIR! SHE'S CLOSE BEHIND AND DRAWING UP FAST. WE'VE GOT HER IN VISION ON NO. 2 SCREEN.

FLAGRANT FLOUTING OF MY PERSONAL ORDERS! GIVE ME SOUND! SOMEBODY'S GOING TO SUFFER FOR THIS!

TWO SHIPS ARE BETTER THAN ONE, SIR HUBERT!

IN 'LODESTAR', DIGBY AND FLAMER ARE CONGRATULATING THEM-SELVES ON THE SUCCESS OF THEIR PLAN, WHEN...

APART FROM 'SPEEDSTAR', THIS IS THE FASTEST SHIP IN ELITE SQUADRON.

IF ONLY WE KNEW WHAT'S HAPPENING AT XQY!

I CAN SEE THEIR ROCKET-BLAST, HANK! YOU'D BETTER CALL UP SIR HUBERT AND...

'SPEEDSTAR' CALLING 'LODESTAR'!

TOO LATE! HE'S GOT IN FIRST!

LAFAYETTE! HOGAN! WHAT'S THE MEANING OF THIS OUTRAGEOUS DISOBEDIENCE?

'ORRIBLE 'UBERT!

JEEPERS!

MAD AS A HORNET!

DEEG! IT WAS YOUR IDEA — YOU EXPLAIN!

SO YOU SEE, SIR, WE COULDN'T STAY OUT OF THIS OPERATION...

I'LL HAVE YOU ALL COURT-MARTIALLED FOR THIS — AND CADET SPRY DRUMMED OUT OF 'ASTRAL'! PUT LAFAYETTE ON!

MEANWHILE, IN THE MEKON'S FLAGSHIP...

THE COURSE IS SET FOR THE RUINED CITY OF MEKONTA, O MASTER.

IT IS WELL! I SHALL RETIRE TO MY PRIVATE QUARTERS TO COMPLETE MY PLAN. GUARD THE PRISONERS WELL!

FAT CHANCE WE'VE GOT OF ESCAPING!

PUT THEM IN THE BOMB-BAY! ONLY ONE GUARD IS NECESSARY!

IT SHALL BE DONE!

THIS LOOKS LIKE THE PAY-OFF!

HIDDEN IN THE VERY SPOT CHOSEN AS A TEMPORARY PRISON FOR HIS FRIENDS, DAN DARE WAITS TENSELY FOR THE HATCH OF THE BOMB-BAY TO OPEN. WILL HE ESCAPE DISCOVERY? NEXT WEEK'S INSTALMENT WILL TELL YOU!

FOURPENCE-HALFPENNY

EVERY WEDNESDAY

EAGLE

COMPANION TO GIRL, SWIFT AND ROBIN

7 JANUARY 1955 Vol. 6 No. 1

DAN DARE
PILOT OF THE FUTURE
PRISONERS OF SPACE

SO THE FOOLISH XALTO BELIEVES THE EARTHMAN DARE STILL LIVES?

DARE IS DEAD — AND SOON WE SHALL SEND YOU TO JOIN HIM.

SOONER THAN YOU THINK, YOU GREEN GHOULS!

AS THE MEKON'S PRISONERS DESCEND INTO THE BOMB-BAY, IT SEEMS CERTAIN THAT DAN DARE WILL BE DISCOVERED!

THE STORY SO FAR:
The Mekon, having destroyed space station XQY with a time-bomb, orders his Chief Pilot to set course for the ruins of the City of Mekonta, on the planet Venus, where, supported by his rebel Treens, the Mekon hopes to rally the Treen population to his evil cause. Dan Dare, whom the Mekon believes to be dead, hides in the bomb-bay of the Treen flagship, unaware that it is about to be used as a cell for his captive friends. As the hatch opens to admit Groupie, Steve and Xalto, Dan tenses himself for action.

G-GREAT G-GALAXIES! WH-WHAT'S THAT?

STEADY, GROUPIE! THERE'S NOTHING DOWN THERE TO HURT YOU!

GULP!

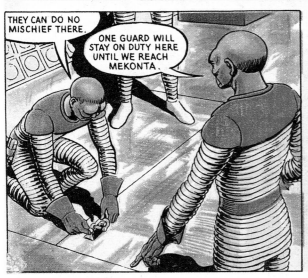

THEY CAN DO NO MISCHIEF THERE.

ONE GUARD WILL STAY ON DUTY HERE UNTIL WE REACH MEKONTA.

COLONEL DARE — BY ALL THAT'S MARVELLOUS!

NOW I'LL BELIEVE ANYTHING!

AS THE BOMB WENT OUT — I GOT IN!

IT IS TRULY YOU, O EARTHMAN! WHAT IS THIS MAGIC YOU POSSESS WHICH ALWAYS BRINGS YOU BACK TO FIGHT AGAIN?

PLAIN LUCK, XALTO — PLUS AN UNDYING HATRED OF ALL THAT YOUR EX-MASTER, THE MEKON, STANDS FOR!

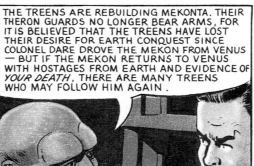

I CAN'T SEE HOW WE'RE ANY BETTER OFF HERE THAN WE WERE IN THAT PERISHING SOLAR-CELL.

STOP GROUSING, GROUPIE! WE'RE *TOGETHER* AGAIN AND COLONEL DARE WILL THINK OF SOMETHING BEFORE WE REACH MEKONTA.

MEKONTA? DON'T TELL ME THE MEKON'S MAKING FOR VENUS!

THE TREENS ARE REBUILDING MEKONTA. THEIR THERON GUARDS NO LONGER BEAR ARMS, FOR IT IS BELIEVED THAT THE TREENS HAVE LOST THEIR DESIRE FOR EARTH CONQUEST SINCE COLONEL DARE DROVE THE MEKON FROM VENUS — BUT IF THE MEKON RETURNS TO VENUS WITH HOSTAGES FROM EARTH AND EVIDENCE OF *YOUR DEATH*, THERE ARE MANY TREENS WHO MAY FOLLOW HIM AGAIN.

NOT IF *I* CAN STOP IT! HOW LONG BEFORE WE REACH VENUS, XALTO?

IN ABOUT THREE EARTH-HOURS FROM NOW.

WILL "ELITE" SQUADRON CATCH UP WITH US BY THEN, COLONEL DARE?

NOT A HOPE BUT *THAT'S* NOT WHAT'S WORRYING ME.

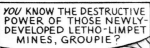

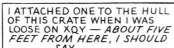

YOU KNOW THE DESTRUCTIVE POWER OF THOSE NEWLY-DEVELOPED LETHO-LIMPET MINES, GROUPIE?

THEY'RE MINIATURE MURDER! WHAT ABOUT 'EM?

I ATTACHED ONE TO THE HULL OF THIS CRATE WHEN I WAS LOOSE ON XQY — *ABOUT FIVE FEET FROM HERE, I SHOULD SAY.*

GALLOPING GREMLINS!

TALK ABOUT "OUT-OF-THE-FRYING-PAN-INTO-THE-FIRE"! *WHAT TIME DID YOU SET IT FOR?*

RATHER LESS THAN THREE HOURS FROM NOW — SO LET'S HOPE THE MEKON MAKES GOOD TIME TO VENUS.

MEANWHILE, IN AREA "X", CLOSE TO THE COSMIC CLOUD WHICH ONCE WAS SPACE STATION XQY, THE SOUND CHANNEL BETWEEN 'SPEEDSTAR' AND 'LODESTAR' FAIRLY SIZZLES AS SIR HUBERT GUEST GIVES TONGUE.

I OUGHT TO ORDER 'LODESTAR' STRAIGHT BACK TO BASE AND PUT THOSE SCRAP-HAPPY LUNATICS UNDER CLOSE ARREST!

THINK, SIR HUBERT! THE MEKON HAS THREE SUPER-ARMED SHIPS OF FANTASTIC RANGE AND SPEED. 'SPEEDSTAR' COULD NEVER HOPE TO FIGHT SINGLE-HANDED.

BUT WITH 'LODESTAR' IN SUPPORT, WE WOULD AT LEAST HAVE A FIGHTING CHANCE.

'SPEEDSTAR' TO 'LODESTAR'! CONTROLLER CALLING! YOU WILL TAKE YOUR POSITION ABREAST OF US TO PORT AND, UPON OUR COUNT, PROCEED AT MAXIMUM THRUST...

...AND HEAVEN HELP YOU ALL WHEN I GET YOU BACK TO H.Q. — IF EVER!

IN 'LODESTAR', SIR HUBERT'S ORDERS ARE RECEIVED WITH MIXED FEELINGS. MAJOR/PILOT LAFAYETTE — ADIEU! SPACEMAN PIERRE — SECOND-CLASS —'ELLO! STAND BY FOR *ULTRA-BOOST MISTER HOGAN!*

MY ONE AND ONLY NIGHTMARE IS TO BE "GROUNDED" — AND IT LOOKS LIKE COMING TRUE!

WE'RE IN, DIGBY SIR!

IT WON'T BE LONG BEFORE WE'RE *OUT OF SPACEFLEET,* YOUNG FLAMER!

AS THE TWO CRACK SPACESHIPS DRAW AWAY FROM THE REST OF "ELITE" SQUADRON IN THE WAKE OF THE MEKON'S FLEET, DAN AND HIS CHUMS COUNT THE MINUTES...

HOW LONG, O EARTHMAN?

NINETY MINUTES, XALTO.

FIVE THOUSAND FOUR HUNDRED SECONDS AND THEN *BOOOMP!*

CHEER UP, GROUPIE! IF WE DON'T TOUCH DOWN ON VENUS FIRST, WE'LL NEVER LIVE TO COUNT DOWN TO ZERO! LET'S SING!

SURELY THESE EARTH-LINGS HAVE INFECTED XALTO WITH THEIR OWN MADNESS, FOR EVEN *HE* HAS LEARNED TO SING IN THE VERY FACE OF DEATH!

SPREAD YOUR WINGS!

AS THE LETHO-LIMPET BOMB TICKS OFF THE SECONDS, THE MEKON'S FLAGSHIP RACES TOWARDS VENUS. WILL SHE MAKE HER LAND-FALL ON THE GREAT PLAIN OF MEKONTA BEFORE THE TIME-DEVICE RIPS HER HULL TO RIBBONS? WATCH OUT FOR NEXT WEEK'S EXCITING EPISODE!

FOURPENCE-HALFPENNY

EVERY WEDNESDAY

EAGLE

COMPANION TO GIRL, SWIFT AND ROBIN

14 JANUARY 1955 Vol. 6 No. 2

DAN DARE
PILOT OF THE FUTURE
PRISONERS OF SPACE

'SPEEDSTAR' TO 'LODESTAR'! STAND BY TO TRANSFER SPACEMAN DIGBY AND CADET SPRY TO US — WE ARE COMING ALONGSIDE!

INTO THE LION'S DEN, FLAMER!

I'LL FEEL A LOT HAPPIER WHEN I'VE GOT THAT YOUNGSTER *HERE* — UNDER MY OWN EYE!

WELL, HE CAN'T *EAT* US!

'LODESTAR' TO 'SPEEDSTAR'! ORDERS RECEIVED AND UNDERSTOOD!

THE STORY SO FAR : Whilst Steve, Groupie, Xalto and Dan, imprisoned in the bomb-bay of the Mekon's flagship, wait helplessly for a limpet-mine to explode, 'Speedstar' and 'Lodestar' reach area 'X' and find that nothing remains of satellite XQY except a cloud of radio-active particles. With reactor-brakes belching, the two Earthships draw alongside.

I'M GETTING MASSIVE REACTION FROM THE EXTERIOR GEIGERS, SIR HUBERT. WE'RE CLOSE TO A FIELD OF INTENSE RADIO-ACTIVITY !

THE REMAINS OF XQY, NO DOUBT! THE MEKON MADE A THOROUGH JOB OF IT WITH HIS HORROR BOMB BEFORE HE TOOK OFF FOR VENUS!

COLONEL DARE TOLD US TO WATCH OUT FOR HIS PERSONAL IDENTITY FLARES WHEN WE ARRIVED HERE.

I KNOW, SONDAR — BUT IF HE WAS *OUTSIDE* XQY WHEN THAT BOMB BLASTED OFF, I'M AFRAID HE'S . . .

DON'T SAY IT, SIR! I JUST *WON'T* BELIEVE COLONEL DARE'S HAD IT!

No.1 AIR LOCK

NEITHER WILL *I*!

SO...! I'LL HAVE *PLENTY* TO SAY TO YOU TWO WHEN THIS "OP" IS OVER! MEANWHILE, YOU'LL GET AFT AND STAY THERE!

YES, SIR!

CONTROLLER TO 'LODESTAR'! WE'RE PROCEEDING AT MAXIMUM SPEED IN PURSUIT OF MEKON'S FLEET, WHICH IS BELIEVED VENUS-BOUND. *STAY WITH US!*

WOW! LET'S GO BEFORE HE BUSTS THAT SPEAKER — AND MY EAR-DRUMS, PIERRE!

ALREADY HE HAS BUST THE CAREERS OF TWO PROMISING SPACEFLEET OFFICERS, HANK!

MEANWHILE, IN THE BOMB-BAY OF THE MEKON'S FLAGSHIP, WITH ONLY THE THICKNESS OF THE HULL BETWEEN THEM AND THE TICKING LIMPET-MINE OUTSIDE, DAN DARE AND HIS FRIENDS COUNT THE MINUTES!

HOW LONG, COLONEL DARE ?

I MAKE IT FORTY-FIVE MINUTES AND SEVENTEEN SECONDS, STEVE.

FORGET THE ODD SECONDS! THREE-QUARTERS OF AN HOUR WILL SEE US *OUT*!

LET'S FACE IT! IF COLONEL DARE'S LIMPET-MINE BLOWS UP *BEFORE* WE TOUCH DOWN ON VENUS, WE'VE *ALL* HAD IT — INCLUDING THE MEKON. BUT IF WE *DO* MAKE A LANDFALL FIRST, WHAT'S THE DRILL?

I'M HOPING THE MEKON WILL HAVE YOU PARADED *BEFORE* WE REACH VENUS. IF SO, YOU MAY ALL BE CLEAR OF THIS SHIP BEFORE THE EXPLOSION.

WHAT ABOUT *YOU*?

I'LL STICK IT HERE UNTIL A FEW MINUTES BEFORE ZERO HOUR AND THEN TAKE A CHANCE ON GETTING CLEAR OF THE BLAST AREA BEFORE THE BALLOON GOES UP.

ACTION STATIONS! STAND BY REACTOR-JETS FOR LANDING!

SO I RETURN TO MEKONTA — MY KINGDOM! BRING THE EARTH PRISONERS AND XALTO!

AT ONCE, O MIGHTY ONE!

AS THE MEKON'S FLEET APPROACHES MEKONTA IN THE NORTHERN HEMISPHERE OF VENUS, EARTH'S WARNING HAS BEEN RECEIVED AT THE THERON CAPITAL, BEYOND THE FLAME-BELT IN THE SOUTH OF THE PLANET.

WE BELIEVED STRIFE HAD CEASED ON VENUS, BUT IF THE REPORT FROM EARTH IS CORRECT, THERE MAY BE GRAVE TROUBLE WITH THE TREENS WHO ARE REBUILDING MEKONTA.

THE RETURN OF THE MEKON MAY ROUSE MANY OF THEM TO REBELLION!

THE TOKEN FORCE GUARDING THE TREENS ARE NOT EVEN ARMED.

THEY WILL HAVE NO CHANCE AGAINST THE MEKON'S RENEGADES.

AS THE THERON COMBAT SHIPS SCREAM NORTHWARDS, THE MEKON'S FLEET MAKES ITS LANDFALL . . .

THERE BLOW THE REACTORS! WE'RE TOUCHING DOWN WITH SEVEN MINUTES TO SPARE!

MY LUCKY NUMBER!

REACTORS AT MAXIMUM! STAND BY FOR TOUCH-DOWN!

I HAVE WAITED LONG FOR THIS MOMENT!

LOOK! *IT IS* THE FLAGSHIP OF THE MIGHTY MEKON! HE HAS RETURNED TO US!

WILL THE TREEN POPULATION OF MEKONTA RALLY TO THEIR OLD LEADER? AND CAN DAN DARE AND HIS FRIENDS ESCAPE FROM THE FLAGSHIP BEFORE THE LIMPET-MINE BLOWS IT TO ATOMS? WATCH FOR NEXT WEEK'S EXCITING EPISODE!

FOURPENCE-HALFPENNY

EVERY WEDNESDAY

EAGLE

COMPANION TO GIRL, SWIFT AND ROBIN

28 JANUARY 1955 Vol. 6 No. 4

DAN DARE
PILOT OF THE FUTURE
PRISONERS OF SPACE

THE STORY SO FAR: Having destroyed space station XQY, the Mekon's rebel fleet reaches Venus, where the Treen population is rebuilding the City of Mekonta. When the Mekon produces his Earth prisoners, Steve and Groupie, and announces the death of Dan Dare, the Treen workers rally round their former master and overpower all their Theron guards. Steve, Groupie and Xalto, Dan's Treen ally and formerly the Mekon's Chief Guard, create a diversion by making a dash for freedom, which enables Dan, who was hiding in the Mekon's flag-ship, to leave unseen. As he readjusts the limpet-mine on the hull, Dan is attacked from behind by two Treens . . .

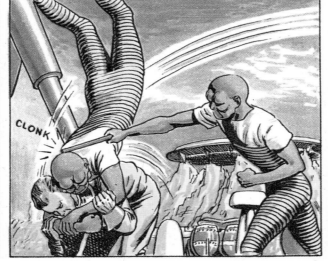

CLONK

DROP IT!

THE EARTHMAN DARE!

IN THE FLESH!

A BRIEF SQUIRT OF PARALYZING GAS STOPS DAN'S ATTACKER IN HIS TRACKS . . .

JUST IN CASE YOU START SPREADING THE JOYFUL NEWS THAT I'M STILL ALIVE AND KICKING, MY FRIEND!

TIME TO TAKE COVER, BROTHER DARE!

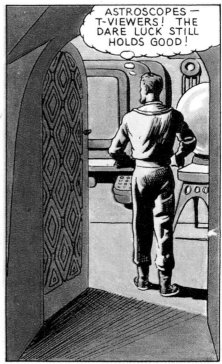

FOURPENCE-HALFPENNY

EVERY WEDNESDAY

EAGLE

COMPANION TO GIRL, SWIFT AND ROBIN

4 FEBRUARY 1955 Vol. 6 No. 5

DAN DARE
PILOT OF THE FUTURE
PRISONERS OF SPACE

DO NOT ATTEMPT TO LAND AT MEKONTA! THE MEKON IS IN CONTROL HERE! MAKE FOR THERON TERRITORY!

THE STORY SO FAR:
The ruthless Mekon, accompanied by a strong force of rebel Treens, returns to Mekonta, his old capital city on Venus. After overthrowing their Theron guards, the Treen population, engaged on rebuilding Mekonta, rally to their ex-master's evil cause. The Mekon's three prisoners Steve Valiant, old Groupie and Xalto, Dan Dare's Treen ally and formerly the Mekon's Chief Guard make a sudden dash for freedom, thus enabling Dan to escape from his hiding-place in the rebel Treen flagship. In the vast, underground system beneath the ruined city, Dan discovers the Communications Room and calls up Sir Hubert Guest in 'Speedstar', the leading ship of Spacefleet's 'Elite' Squadron, which is speeding towards Venus.

HOLD IT, DAN! I'VE ALREADY ALERTED THERON H.Q. THEIR SHIPS ARE ON THE WAY TO MEKONTA RIGHT NOW!

DO ALL YOU CAN TO HEAD THEM OFF! I'VE GOT TO TAKE COVER — THE MEKON'S MOB ARE COMING! SIGNING OFF!

BUT, AS DAN SWITCHES OFF THE ASTROSCOPE, HE FAILS TO NOTICE . . .

SCAN EARTH APPROACHES! PLOT THE EXACT POSITION OF THE SPACEFLEET SQUADRON!

PHEW! JUST AS WELL THE MILDEWED MONSTER DOESN'T KNOW THE EXACT POSITION OF DAN DARE!

SEE, MASTER! THEY CHANGE COURSE AND HEAD FOR THE SOUTH, BEYOND THE FLAME-BELT.

KEEP THEM IN VIEW! IT MAY BE A TRICK!

AS THE TWO EARTH SHIPS SHEER AWAY FROM THE DREAD NORTHERN HEMISPHERE OF VENUS, THEY CROSS COURSES WITH THE ONCOMING THERON FLEET.

SPACEFLEET TO THERONS! GUEST CALLING! MEKONTA LANDING SUICIDAL!

"...REQUEST ESCORT BACK TO YOUR BASE!"

IT IS THE VOICE OF THE EARTH CONTROLLER! SIGNAL ALL SHIPS TO STAND BY FOR CHANGE OF PLAN!

LOOK, MASTER! THE EARTH SHIPS AND THERON FLEET ARE IN RETREAT!

SUFFERING SATELLITES! THEY'VE TURNED-TAIL, STEVE! THEY'RE LEAVING US HERE TO...

IF THEY HAD TOUCHED DOWN HERE IN MEKONTA, THAT TREEN RABBLE WOULD HAVE MADE SHORT WORK OF 'EM.

BUT HOW COULD THEY KNOW THE MEKON'S IN COMMAND HERE?

COLONEL DARE'S WORK FOR A CERT! DON'T FORGET HE'S STILL ON THE LOOSE SOMEWHERE NOT FAR AWAY — THOUGH, LUCKILY, OLD GREEN BEAN DOESN'T KNOW IT YET!

BUT EVEN AS STEVE SPEAKS, THE MEKON'S CHIEF PILOT FINDS THE VITAL CLUE DROPPED BY DAN!

MASTER! THIS IS AN EARTH TIME-PIECE! HOW COMES IT HERE?

GIVE IT TO ME!

TO COLONEL DAN TO MARK THE TIME WE PAID OFF THE MEKON "Digby"

WHAT MAD EARTH TRICK IS THIS? A DEAD MAN'S WATCH — YET STILL IT TICKS!

BUT, SOMEWHERE IN THE GREAT UNDERGROUND NETWORK BENEATH MEKONTA, DAN DARE MOVES STEALTHILY ON HIS LONE MISSION TO RESCUE HIS CHUMS AND DEFEAT THE MEKON! DON'T MISS NEXT WEEK'S THRILLS!

FOURPENCE-HALFPENNY

EVERY WEDNESDAY

EAGLE

COMPANION TO GIRL, SWIFT AND ROBIN

11 FEBRUARY 1955 Vol. 6 No. 6

DAN DARE
PILOT OF THE FUTURE
PRISONERS OF SPACE

IT IS IMPOSSIBLE! DARE *CANNOT* BE ALIVE.

YET THAT'S HIS WATCH YOU HOLD IN YOUR HAND...

AND ITS EVERY TICK BRINGS YOU CLOSER TO THE END OF YOUR ROPE, MEKON!

THE STORY SO FAR: In the vast, underground shelters beneath the Venusian city of Mekonta, Dan Dare makes astroscope contact with Sir Hubert Guest in 'Speedstar' and warns him against landing in Treen territory, because the dread Mekon and his rebel Treens have returned, overthrown the Theron guards and regained the support of the inhabitants. As the Mekon, who believes Dan is dead, and his bodyguard enter the Communications Room, Dan dives for cover, but fails to notice that his wristwatch, inscribed with his name, has fallen off. A few moments later, the Mekon's Chief Pilot discovers the watch, *which is still ticking!* Baffled and furious, the Mekon turns on his prisoners – Groupie, Steve and Xalto.

TREENS! THRICE THE MEKON HAS 'DESTROYED' THE EARTHMAN DARE, *BUT EACH TIME HE HAS RETURNED!*

DARE IS HERE, EVEN NOW, IN MEKONTA! AND WHEN HE STRIKES, THE REIGN OF THE MEKON WILL FINISH FOREVER!

SILENCE, TRAITOROUS DOG!

ARRRGH!

WOP!

YOU BRUTE!

SHALL I END HIS WORTHLESS LIFE, O MASTER?

NOT YET! FROM ONE OF THESE THREE I *MUST* LEARN THE TRUTH!

IF BY SOME BLACK TRICKERY MY ARCH-ENEMY DARE STILL LIVES, HE MUST BE FOUND BEFORE HE DOES FURTHER HARM TO MY PLANS.

IF DARE BE HERE, HE CANNOT ESCAPE — THERE ARE GUARDS AT EVERY OUTLET!

BRING THE EARTH PRISONERS FORWARD! *THEY* SHALL LEAD THE SEARCH!

WHAT'S HE MEAN BY THAT, STEVE?

THEY'RE GOING TO USE US AS A SHIELD, GROUPIE. THE MEKON KNOWS DAN WON'T SHOOT WHILE WE'RE IN THE LINE OF FIRE!

FOURPENCE-HALFPENNY

EVERY WEDNESDAY

EAGLE

COMPANION TO GIRL, SWIFT AND ROBIN

18 FEBRUARY 1955 Vol. 6 No. 7

DAN DARE
PILOT OF THE FUTURE
PRISONERS OF SPACE

NOW COLONEL DARE MUST CHOOSE BETWEEN A SLOW, AGONIZING DEATH OR COMPLETE SURRENDER!

DEADLOCK! I CAN'T GET OUT — AND THEY CAN'T GET IN!

THE STORY SO FAR:
The ruthless Mekon returns to Mekonta, his old capital city on Venus, and the Treens, after overthrowing their Theron guards, rally to their ex-master's evil cause. Dan escapes from the Mekon's flagship and finds the Communications Room beneath the city. He calls up Sir Hubert Guest, hurrying to the rescue in 'Speedstar', and warns him to avoid Treen territory. Meanwhile, Xalto and Steve anger the Mekon, who discovers that Dan is still alive, and are knocked senseless. Taking Groupie with him, the Mekon pursues Dan Dare through Mekonta's underground passages until he takes refuge behind a door. The Mekon gloats as he sees that Dan's 'refuge' is really a small gas-chamber!

NOW I SHALL PROVE THE EARTHMAN IS NOT IMMORTAL! TURN ON THE GAS!

AS THE DEADLY PURPLE GAS SEEPS SLOWLY INTO THE CHAMBER, DAN'S HEAD REELS AND A STRANGE NUMBNESS ATTACKS HIS LIMBS . . .

WHAT THE DICKENS . . . ?

GAS!

SORRY, STEVE — GROUPIE — I DID MY BEST . . .

CALLING COLONEL DARE!

" . . . MAKE YOUR CHOICE! DIE WHERE YOU LIE, OR COME FORTH TO FACE THE FATE I HAVE PLANNED FOR YOU! THE DOOR IS UNLOCKED! YOU HAVE ONLY TO PUSH IT OPEN!"

IS IT BETTER TO PERISH HERE NOW — OR DIE LATER UNDER TORTURE ? I — CAN'T — THINK . . .

FOURPENCE-HALFPENNY

EVERY WEDNESDAY

EAGLE

COMPANION TO GIRL, SWIFT AND ROBIN

25 FEBRUARY 1955 Vol. 6 No. 8

DAN DARE
PILOT OF THE FUTURE
PRISONERS OF SPACE

SO ENDS DARE — THE FOOL WHO DARED DEFY ME!

WAIT! THERE IS MOVEMENT WITHIN!

YOU MURDEROUS DEMONS!

THE STORY SO FAR: The ruthless Mekon returns to Mekonta, his old capital on Venus, and the Treens, after overthrowing their Theron guards, rally to their ex-master's evil cause. After finding the Communications Centre beneath the city, Dan calls up Sir Hubert Guest, hurrying to the rescue in 'Speedstar', and warns him to avoid Treen territory. Leaving Steve and Xalto under guard, the Mekon and his bodyguard, dragging Groupie with them, pursue Dan, who eventually makes the mistake of hiding in a gas-chamber. The Mekon orders his henchmen to turn on the gas, and tells Dan to come out or be killed by the fumes. His head reeling, Dan attempts to reach the door before the gas completes its deadly work.

WHILE — THERE'S LIFE — THERE'S — HOPE! I'VE GOT TO MAKE IT!

WATCH HIM — AND SHUT THAT DOOR!

DAN!

GIVE ME THE HONOUR OF ENDING HIS MISERABLE LIFE, O MASTER!

DAN!

HE LIVES! REVIVE HIM!

G-GROUPIE...

WAKE, EARTHMAN! A WORSE FATE AWAITS YOU!

DAN'S CAPTURE IS WATCHED BY STEVE AND XALTO, WHO HAVE OVERPOWERED THEIR TREEN GUARD.

HE IS STILL ALIVE!

WHAT A MAN! COME ON, XALTO — WE'VE WORK TO DO!

FOURPENCE-HALFPENNY

EVERY WEDNESDAY

EAGLE

COMPANION TO GIRL, SWIFT AND ROBIN

4 MARCH 1955 Vol. 6 No. 9

DAN DARE
PILOT OF THE FUTURE
PRISONERS OF SPACE

STEVE VALIANT REPORTING! *THE MEKON'S CAPTURED COLONEL DARE!*

EARTHLING!

THE STORY SO FAR:

The ruthless Mekon returns to Mekonta, his old capital on Venus, and the Treens, after overthrowing their Theron guards, rally to their ex-master's evil cause. After finding the Communications Centre beneath the city, Dan calls up Sir Hubert Guest, hurrying to the rescue in 'Speedstar', and warns him to avoid Treen territory. The Mekon, dragging Groupie with him, pursues Dan and traps him in a gas-chamber. Weakened by exposure to the deadly gas, Dan staggers out and is captured by the Mekon. Meanwhile, Steve Valiant and Xalto, who have overpowered their guard, call up Sir Hubert Guest, who is anxiously awaiting Dan Dare's instructions at the Theron H.Q. across the flame-belt on Venus.

WE ARE DOOMED — THE MEKON APPROACHES!

THE GAME'S UP, SIR HUBERT! THERE IS NOTHING LEFT TO DO BUT ATTACK IN FULL FORCE—LEAVING US TO TAKE OUR CHANCE! *SIGNING OFF!*

STEVE! *STEVE!* HE'S GONE.

TIME *WE* WERE GONE, TOO! WE'VE GOT TO GET COLONEL DAN *OUT* OF THIS MESS!

WE'VE NO CHOICE NOW BUT TO GO AND BLAST MEKONTA. IT MAY RESULT IN THE DEATH OF OUR FRIENDS, BUT THE MEKON AND HIS GANG *MUST BE WIPED OUT!*

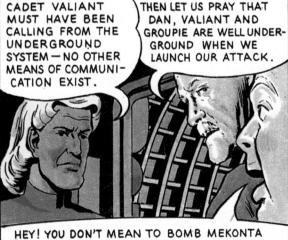

CADET VALIANT MUST HAVE BEEN CALLING FROM THE UNDERGROUND SYSTEM—NO OTHER MEANS OF COMMUNICATION EXIST.

THEN LET US PRAY THAT DAN, VALIANT AND GROUPIE ARE WELL UNDERGROUND WHEN WE LAUNCH OUR ATTACK.

HEY! YOU DON'T MEAN TO BOMB MEKONTA — *NOT WHILE COLONEL DAN'S THERE?*

YOU DON'T EXPECT ME TO APPROACH MEKONTA FLYING *A WHITE FLAG*, DO YOU, SPACEMAN DIGBY?

N-N-NO, SIR!

DAN IS LIKE MY OWN SON. D'YOU THINK I *LIKE* THE IDEA OF RISKING KILLING HIM?

WITHIN MINUTES OF STEVE'S CALL, 'ELITE' SQUADRON AND THE THERON BATTLE FLEET ARE SPEEDING TOWARDS MEKONTA.

IN MEKONTA . . .

CHEER UP, XALTO — WE'LL GO DOWN WITH COLOURS FLYING!

STAY, MASTER!

XALTO AND THE YOUNG EARTHLING CALLED "VALIANT" HAVE VANISHED AND "HE" SET TO GUARD THEM LIES UNCONSCIOUS— HIS RAY-GUN GONE!

SO! LET COLONEL DARE AND THE OLD EARTHLING ENTER THIS DOOR FIRST!

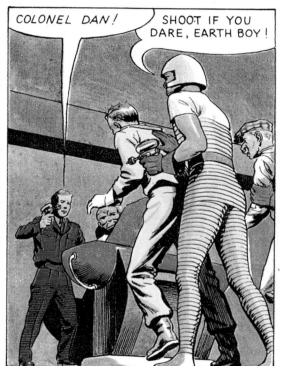

COLONEL DAN!

SHOOT IF YOU DARE, EARTH BOY!

NO DOUBT THIS MEDDLING YOUNG FOOL HAS BEEN IN CONTACT WITH EARTH FORCES — SWITCH ON THE ASTROSCOPE!

COLONEL DARE! ARE YOU ALL RIGHT?

THE GREEN GHOULS GASSED HIM, STEVE!

THE EARTH SQUADRON AND THERON BATTLE FLEET! THEY HEAD THIS WAY, MASTER!

THEN WE SHALL GIVE THEM A TARGET FOR THEIR ATTACK!

BRING THE PRISONERS AND FOLLOW ME!

STAKE THEM DOWN! WHEN SIR HUBERT GUEST DROPS DEATH FROM THE SKIES, THEY SHALL BE THE *FIRST* TO DIE!

YOU'LL PAY FOR THIS, YOU LITTLE GREEN DEMON!

WHAT NOW, MASTER?

LOOK UP, EARTHMEN, INTO THE FACE OF THE DEATH *YOUR OWN FRIENDS BRING YOU!*

PREPARE FOR INSTANT TAKE-OFF! WE WILL WATCH THIS COMEDY FROM ABOVE!

WITH EARTH AND THERON BATTLE FLEETS FAST APPROACHING TO BOMB MEKONTA, WHAT CHANCE HAVE DAN DARE AND HIS COMPANIONS OF SURVIVAL? DON'T MISS NEXT WEEK'S EXCITING EPISODE!

FOURPENCE-HALFPENNY

EVERY WEDNESDAY

EAGLE

COMPANION TO GIRL, SWIFT AND ROBIN

11 MARCH 1955 Vol. 6 No. 10

THE STORY SO FAR:
The ruthless Mekon, accompanied by a force of rebel Treens, returns to Mekonta, his old capital city on Venus. After overthrowing their Theron guards, the Treen population rally to their ex-master's evil cause. Learning that the city is about to be attacked from the air, the Mekon has his prisoners – Dan Dare, Steve Valiant, old Groupie and Xalto, Dan's Treen ally and formerly the Mekon's Chief Guard – staked to the ground in the centre of Mekonta. Unaware of this, Earth's 'Elite' squadron, led by Sir Hubert Guest, and the Theron battle-fleet are speeding across the flame-belt which encircles Venus, to bomb the rebel Treen city and destroy the Mekon and his bodyguard. The Mekon prepares to leave Dan and his three friends to their grim fate.

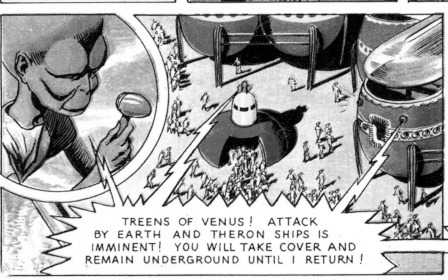

AS THE MEKON'S SHIPS TAKE OFF FROM MEKONTA, THE COMBINED EARTH AND THERON FLEET SCREAMS HIGH ABOVE THE FLAME-BELT ON *ITS* GRIM MISSION OF RETRIBUTION . . .

. . . AND IN THE LEADING SHIP, *'SPEEDSTAR'* . . .

ONE SINGLE GUIDED MISSILE OF "MULTUM MARK V" CLASS SHOULD CLEAR MEKONTA SUFFICIENTLY FOR US TO LAND.

'SPEEDSTAR' WILL MAKE THE RUN AND LAUNCH THE MISSILE. ALL OTHER SHIPS WILL STAY CLEAR OF THE AREA UNTIL WE TOUCH DOWN AND RADIO FURTHER ORDERS!

"MULTUM MARK V!" ARE WE CARRYING ONE OF *THOSE* MURDER-MACHINES IN THIS CRATE, SIR?

OUR SMALL STOCK-PILE WAS MADE FOR AN EMERGENCY SUCH AS THIS. AS THEY CREATE NO RADIO-ACTIVITY, IT WILL BE SAFE FOR US TO FOLLOW DOWN IMMEDIATELY.

COLONEL DAN'S IN MEKONTA! UNLESS HE'S TUCKED AWAY IN THE DEEPEST SHELTER, HE HASN'T A *HOPE!* *NOBODY'S* GOING TO LAUNCH THAT THING WHILE I'M ALIVE TO STOP HIM!

BE CALM, MY FRIEND — NO GOOD CAN COME OF MUTINY!

LET GO!

I'M SORRY, SIR, BUT I! . . .

I UNDERSTAND! *MINE* WILL BE THE HAND TO LAUNCH THE MISSILE — AND IF ANYTHING HAPPENS TO DAN OR THE OTHERS, I SHALL RESIGN IMMEDIATELY WE RETURN TO EARTH.

CHIN UP, DIGBY, SIR! TRUST THE WELL-KNOWN "DARE LUCK"!

BUT THE "DARE LUCK" SEEMS TO BE RUNNING OUT FAST!

WE *KNOW* WHAT'S COMING TO US, BUT THAT MILDEWED MONKEY THE MEKON *DOESN'T KNOW WHAT'S* IN STORE FOR HIM!

HE'S *WELL* OUT OF THE DANGER ZONE NOW!

WHAT DO YOU MEAN?

IF 'ELITE' AND THE THERON FLEET TOOK OFF IMMEDIATELY YOU REPORTED MY CAPTURE, THEY SHOULD BE HERE IN APPROXIMATELY TWENTY MINUTES. BUT, *IN EXACTLY THIRTY MINUTES FROM NOW*, THAT LIMPET-MINE I FIXED ON THE MEKON'S FLAGSHIP WILL BLOW HIM AND HIS EVIL BROOD TO SMITHEREENS!

THE HANDS OF DAN DARE'S WATCH MOVE INEXORABLY TOWARDS THE FATAL MOMENT WHEN "MULTUM MARK V" IS DUE TO BRING DEVASTATION TO THE FACE OF MEKONTA! WILL SOME LAST-MINUTE MIRACLE SAVE THE FOUR VICTIMS OF THE MEKON'S HATRED? DON'T MISS NEXT WEEK'S THRILLS!

FOURPENCE-HALFPENNY

EVERY WEDNESDAY

EAGLE

COMPANION TO GIRL, SWIFT AND ROBIN

18 MARCH 1955 Vol. 6 No. 11

DAN DARE

PILOT OF THE FUTURE

PRISONERS OF SPACE

THAT'S 'SPEEDSTAR' !

MAKING A TRIAL RUN . . .

BEFORE SHE LAYS HER EGG — WITH NO CHANCE OF SEEING US, SMACK IN THE MIDDLE OF THE TARGET !

THE STORY SO FAR:
The ruthless Mekon, accompanied by a force of rebel Treens, returns to Mekonta, his old capital city on Venus. After overthrowing their Theron guards, the Treen population rally to their ex-master's evil cause. Learning that the city is about to be attacked from the air, the Mekon has his prisoners – Dan Dare, Steve Valiant, old Groupie and Xalto, Dan's Treen ally and formerly the Mekon's Chief Guard – staked to the ground in the centre of Mekonta. Unaware of this, Earth's 'Elite' squadron, led by Sir Hubert Guest in 'Speedstar', and the Theron battle-fleet approach their target. The Mekon leaves Dan and Co. and takes off in his flagship to witness their destruction from above – but he doesn't realize that a limpet-mine, fixed to his spaceship, is almost due to explode. Meanwhile, the helpless prisoners watch as 'Speedstar' flashes across Mekonta on her test run . . .

I WISH WE'D PASSED IN OUR CHIPS OUT THERE IN DEEP SPACE, RATHER THAN LIKE THIS.

WE AIN'T DEAD YET, STEVE ! I CAN STILL HEAR MY HEART BEATING — GOOD AND LOUD !

I GAVE THE WORD TO SIR HUBERT TO BLAST MEKONTA WHEN I THOUGHT YOU'D HAD IT IN THAT GAS-CHAMBER. IT SEEMED THE ONLY WAY OF WIPING OUT THE MEKON AND HIS GANG.

IF ONLY THAT GREEN GOON WAS HERE TO COP HIS LOT ALONG WITH US, I'D DIE LAUGHING !

I FEEL NO FEAR ! NOTHING CAN DESTROY THE EARTHMAN DARE. HAVE I NOT, WITH MY OWN EYES, SEEN HIM TWICE RETURN FROM DEATH ?

POOR XALTO ! IS IT BETTER TO LET HIM DIE IN BLISSFUL IGNORANCE — OR TO TELL HIM THE TRUTH — THAT "DARE'S LUCK" HAS RUN OUT AT LONG LAST ?

TARGET PLOTTED !

COURSE FIXED !

MISSILE MOUNTED !

ZOOM

AS 'SPEEDSTAR' TURNS BACK ACROSS MEKONTA FOR HER "KILLING RUN", SIR HUBERT GUEST PREPARES TO LAUNCH THE DREAD GUIDED MISSILE—"MULTUM MK. V"!

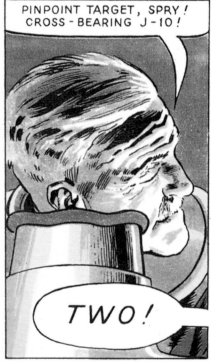

WITH THE DEADLY MISSILE SPEEDING TOWARDS MEKONTA, WILL DAN AND HIS FRIENDS BE DESTROYED BY THE ACTION OF *THEIR OWN COMRADES*? DON'T MISS NEXT WEEK'S THRILLING INSTALMENT!

FOURPENCE-HALFPENNY

EVERY WEDNESDAY

EAGLE

COMPANION TO GIRL, SWIFT AND ROBIN

25 MARCH 1955 Vol. 6 No. 12

DAN DARE
PILOT OF THE FUTURE
PRISONERS OF SPACE

DIVERT MISSILE EIGHTY DEGREES! *JUMP TO IT!*

TOO LATE!

THE STORY SO FAR:
The ruthless Mekon returns to Mekonta, his old capital city on Venus. After overthrowing their Theron guards, the Treens rally to their ex-master's evil cause. Learning that the city is about to be attacked by Earth's 'Elite' squadron, led by Sir Hubert Guest in 'Speedstar', and the Theron battle-fleet, the Mekon has Dan Dare, Steve, Groupie and Xalto staked to the ground in Mekonta's centre and takes off in his flagship to witness their destruction from above, unaware that a limpet-mine fixed to his spaceship is almost due to explode. Dan and Co. watch helplessly as Multum Mark V, a guided missile, is released from 'Speedstar', and Sir Hubert, Digby and Flamer are horrified when they see their friends in the target area!

THIS IS IT, STEVE!

IT'LL BE QUICK, ANYWAY, SIR!

AND WE'LL ALL GO TOGETHER! *CHEERIO!*

IN 'SPEEDSTAR', THE PILOT FRANTICALLY OPERATES THE MISSILE'S GUIDING DEVICE...

..AND THE DEATH-DEALING MISSILE MAKES A SPLIT-SECOND TIGHT TURN AND SHEERS OFF INTO SPACE...

FINIS!

FOURPENCE-HALFPENNY

EVERY WEDNESDAY

EAGLE

COMPANION TO GIRL, SWIFT AND ROBIN

1 APRIL 1955 Vol. 6 No. 13

DAN DARE
PILOT OF THE FUTURE
PRISONERS OF SPACE

KEEP AT IT, XALTO!

THE STORY SO FAR:
The ruthless Mekon returns to Mekonta, his old capital city on Venus. After over-throwing their Theron guards, the Treens rally to their ex-master's evil cause. Learning that the city is about to be attacked by Earth's 'Elite' squadron, led by Sir Hubert Guest in 'Speedstar', and the Theron battle-fleet, the Mekon has Dan Dare, Steve, Groupie and Xalto staked to the ground in Mekonta's centre and takes off in his flagship to witness their destruction from above, unaware that a limpet-mine fixed to his spaceship is almost due to explode. "Multum Mark V", a guided missile, is released from 'Speedstar', but Sir Hubert, Digby and Flamer see their friends below and divert the missile from its course just in time, sending it off into space. As Sir Hubert prepares to land in 'Speedstar', Xalto, the Treen deserter, whose arm has been torn free by the violent passing of the deadly missile, hastens to release his allies.

I WAS RIGHT! AGAIN EARTHMAN DARE DEFIES DEATH AND LIVES TO DEFEAT THE MEKON!

TIME'S ON OUR SIDE NOW!

LOOK! 'SPEEDSTAR'S' USING HER REACTORS!

I DON'T UNDERSTAND, COLONEL DARE.

REMEMBER THAT LIMPET-MINE I FIXED TO THE HULL OF OLD GREENGAGE'S FLAGSHIP?

'SPEEDSTAR'S' TOUCHING DOWN.

JUMPING JETS! I'D FORGOTTEN THAT!

IF THIS TICKER DIGBY GAVE ME IS STILL RUNNING TRUE TO FORM...

...THE MEKON'S GOT EXACTLY TWENTY MINUTES BEFORE THAT MINE BLASTS HIS SHIP, HIS CREW AND HIMSELF TO SMITHEREENS!

SEE — THE EARTHSHIP!

I'LL TEACH 'EM TO SINGE MY WHISKERS!

THE TREEN RABBLE DIVED UNDERGROUND WHEN THE MEKON TOOK OFF!

AND WE'VE GOT TO BOTTLE 'EM UP!

XALTO! GROUPIE! GIVE THE 'GEN' TO SIR HUBERT IMMEDIATELY HE TOUCHES DOWN! COME ON, STEVE!

FOURPENCE-HALFPENNY

EVERY WEDNESDAY

EAGLE

COMPANION TO GIRL, SWIFT AND ROBIN

8 APRIL 1955 Vol. 6 No. 14

DAN DARE
PILOT OF THE FUTURE
PRISONERS OF SPACE

AARRK!

HANDS UP, YOU BRUTES!

STEVE!

GOOD OLD FLAMER!

DAN DARE AND STEVE VALIANT, BATTLING DESPERATELY TO CONTAIN THE REBEL TREENS IN THE UNDERGROUND SHELTERS OF MEKONTA, ARE REINFORCED, IN THE NICK OF TIME, BY THEIR COMRADES — DIGBY, SIR HUBERT, 'FLAMER' SPRY, OLD GROUPIE AND SONDAR.

DAN, MY BOY! THANK HEAVEN WE'RE IN TIME!

ONLY JUST, SIR!

COLONEL DAN!

DIGBY! DRIVE THIS RABBLE BELOW AND FREE THE THERON GUARDS.

AYE, AYE, SIR!

WHERE TO, DAN?

'SPEEDSTAR', SIR! I'VE GOT TO MAKE RADIO CONTACT WITH THE MEKON'S FLAGSHIP!

WE THOUGHT HE WAS GROUNDED HERE.

HE TOOK OFF SHORTLY AFTER STEVE TOLD YOU TO ATTACK.

WHAT'S THE PANIC? THERON BATTLE FLEET AND 'ELITE' SQUADRON ARE GIVING US COMPLETE COVER.

I WANT THE MEKON ALIVE — AND I'VE GOT TEN MINUTES LEFT TO WARN HIM!

WHAT THE DICKENS GOES ON, DAN?

SORRY, SIR — I'LL HAVE TO EXPLAIN LATER! PLEASE MAN THE ASTROSCOPE AND TRY TO PICK UP THE MEKON'S FLIGHT!

FAR OUT IN SPACE, "MULTUM MARK V", RUNNING WILD, POINTS ITS DEADLY WARHEAD DIRECTLY AT ONE OF THE MEKON'S THREE SHIPS.

DARE CALLING MEKON! DARE TO MEKON!

JUMPING JETS! DAN — QUICKLY — LOOK AT THIS!

AS SIR HUBERT GETS THE TREEN SPACECRAFT IN ASTROSCOPIC FOCUS, "MULTUM MARK V" STRIKES HOME!

"MULTUM MARK V"! THE CHANCES OF THAT HAPPENING WERE INCALCULABLE — BUT THE MEKON'S SHIP HAS ESCAPED!

NOT YET, SIR!

DARE CALLING MEKON! THIS IS YOUR LAST CHANCE!

IN THE MEKON'S FLAGSHIP, ROCKED BY THE THERMO-NUCLEAR FISSION WHICH DESTROYED ITS COMPANIONS...

BOTH SHIPS ARE UTTERLY DESTROYED, MASTER — WE ARE ALONE!

MASTER!

BUT WE STILL SURVIVE! NO EARTH OR THERON CRAFT HAS THE SPEED OR RANGE TO REACH US NOW.

DARE CALLS FROM MEKONTA. HIS ACCURSED FACE IS EVEN NOW ON THE SCREEN.

THIS IS NOT THE END, EARTHMAN! WE SHALL MEET AGAIN!

ACROSS LIMITLESS SPACE, DAN DARE FACES EARTH'S ARCH-ENEMY.

LISTEN, MONSTER! UNLESS YOU DO EXACTLY AS I SAY, YOU HAVE ONLY EIGHT EARTH MINUTES TO LIVE!

THE LIMPET-MINE ATTACHED TO THE HULL OF THE MEKON'S FLAGSHIP TICKS AWAY THE FINAL MINUTES! CAN DAN DARE SUCCEED IN SAVING THE LIFE OF THE MEKON AND TAKING HIM PRISONER? *DON'T MISS NEXT WEEK'S FAST-MOVING EPISODE!*

FOURPENCE-HALFPENNY

EVERY WEDNESDAY

EAGLE

COMPANION TO GIRL, SWIFT AND ROBIN

15 APRIL 1955 Vol. 6 No. 15

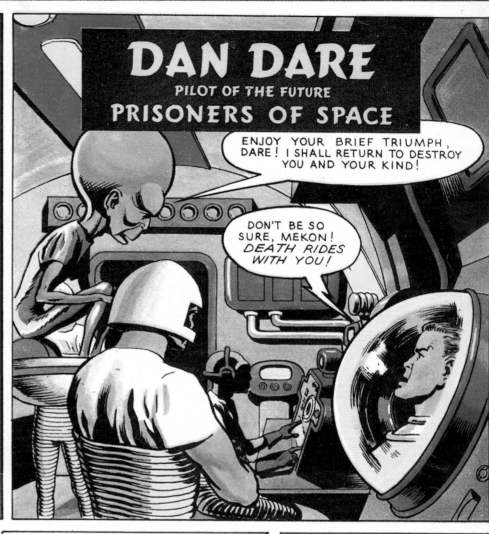

DAN DARE PILOT OF THE FUTURE
PRISONERS OF SPACE

ENJOY YOUR BRIEF TRIUMPH, DARE! I SHALL RETURN TO DESTROY YOU AND YOUR KIND!

DON'T BE SO SURE, MEKON! *DEATH RIDES WITH YOU!*

THE STORY SO FAR:
The ruthless Mekon returns to Mekonta, his old capital city on Venus. After overthrowing their Theron guards, the Treens rally to their ex-master's evil cause. Learning that the city is about to be attacked by Earth's 'Elite' squadron, led by Sir Hubert Guest in 'Speedstar', and the Theron battle-fleet, the Mekon has Dan Dare, Steve, Groupie and Xalto staked to the ground in Mekonta's centre and takes off in his flagship to witness their destruction from above, unaware that a limpet-mine fixed to his spaceship is almost due to explode. "Multum Mark V", a guided missile, is released from 'Speedstar', but is diverted just in time and sent off into space, where it destroys the spaceships accompanying the Mekon's flagship. Dan and Co., now free, are joined by Sir Hubert and the crew of 'Speedstar'. Determined to capture his arch-enemy alive, Dan contacts the fleeing Mekon.

IN ALL OUR PAST ENCOUNTERS, *HAVE YOU EVER KNOWN ME TO LIE?*

THAT IS YOUR WEAKNESS — AND THE REASON *I*, THE MEKON, MUST TRIUMPH IN THE END! I GO TO "ORBIT MORTUS", WHERE NO ENEMY SHIP DARE VENTURE! EVIL FORTUNE ATTEND YOU, COLONEL DARE — *UNTIL WE MEET AGAIN!*

PAY HEED, MEKON! I GIVE YOU MY WORD THAT ATTACHED TO THE OUTER HULL OF YOUR FLAGSHIP IS A LIMPET-MINE!

SO *THAT'S* IT!

I SET ITS TIME-DEVICE WITH MY OWN HAND! THE MOMENT OF FISSION WILL BE *FIVE MINUTES FROM NOW!*

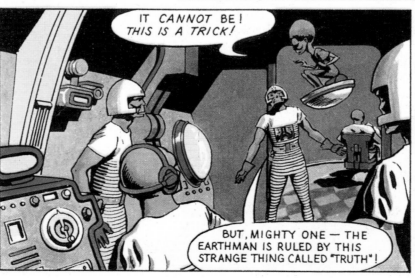

IT *CANNOT BE!* THIS IS A TRICK!

BUT, MIGHTY ONE — THE EARTHMAN IS RULED BY THIS STRANGE THING CALLED "TRUTH"!

PREPARE FOR SPACE DUTY! ALL PERSONNEL WILL SEARCH OUTER HULL IMMEDIATELY!

FOUR MINUTES TO GO, MEKON!

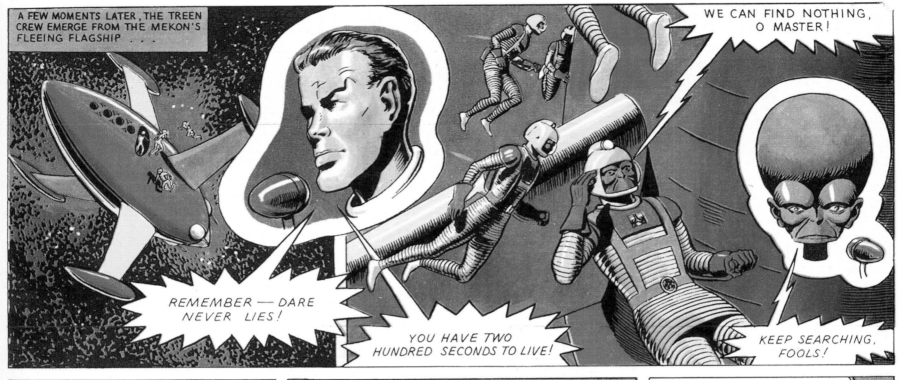

FOURPENCE-HALFPENNY

EVERY WEDNESDAY

EAGLE

COMPANION TO GIRL, SWIFT AND ROBIN

22 APRIL 1955 Vol. 6 No. 16

THE STORY SO FAR: The ruthless Mekon's attempt to regain power on Venus and destroy Dan Dare fails. While the rebel Treens are being rounded up and order is being restored to Mekonta city, Dan, accompanied by Sir Hubert Guest, contacts the fleeing Mekon from 'Speedstar' and warns him that a limpet-mine attached to the hull of his flagship is almost due to explode. Deserted by all save his Chief Pilot, the Mekon must decide between captivity or death. His only chance is to leave the flagship in the solar-cell and wait for his enemies to fetch him in. As Dan awaits the Mekon's decision, Digby, Flamer, Steve, Groupie and Xalto return to 'Speedstar' to report latest developments.

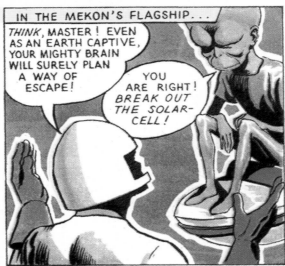

WITH SECONDS TO SPARE, THE SOLAR-CELL IS AUTOMATICALLY LAUNCHED FROM THE BOMB-BAY OF THE MEKON'S FLAGSHIP. AS THE SINISTER SPACE-BUBBLE—WHICH ONCE IMPRISONED STEVE AND GROUPIE—FLOATS FREE, *THE LIMPET-MINE DOES ITS DIRE WORK...*

MY SPACIAL KINGDOM DESTROYED—MY PLANS THWARTED AGAIN—AND BY ONE SINGLE EARTHMAN—*DARE!*

WE LIVE TO FIGHT AGAIN, O MASTER.

AS 'SPEEDSTAR' TAKES OFF FROM MEKONTA...

YOICKS!

TALLY-HO!

THE END OF THE STORY, DAN!

NOT *YET*, SIR HUBERT!

'SPEEDSTAR', SETTING HER COURSE BY RADAR AND ASTROSCOPE, FAST APPROACHES THE SOLAR-CELL...

WE'VE *GOT* HIM!

YOUR COMMAND, COLONEL DARE! *WHAT'S THE DRILL?*

AT LAST!

HE'S *MY* BIRD, SIR! I'M GOING OUT TO GET HIM—AND *TAKING DIGBY WITH ME!*

LOOK OUT, MEKON—*HERE I COME!*

HAS THE GRIM REIGN OF THE MEKON, AT LONG LAST, COME TO AN END? WATCH FOR NEXT WEEK'S EXCITING INSTALMENT OF *PRISONERS OF SPACE!*

FOURPENCE-HALFPENNY

EVERY WEDNESDAY

EAGLE

COMPANION TO GIRL, SWIFT AND ROBIN

29 APRIL 1955 Vol. 6 No. 17

DAN DARE
PILOT OF THE FUTURE
PRISONERS OF SPACE

THE STORY SO FAR:
The ruthless Mekon's attempt to regain power on Venus fails, so he escapes in his flagship. Dan warns him that a limpet-mine, almost due to explode, is attached to the hull. Forced to abandon his flagship in the solar-cell which he designed for Dan Dare's destruction, the Mekon and his Chief Pilot float in space as 'Speedstar' comes alongside. Dan and Digby emerge from the air-lock door to take custody of Earth's arch-enemy, the Mekon himself!

LOOK AT 'EM, COLONEL DAN! "PRISONERS OF SPACE!"

THEY'LL BE PRISONERS OF EARTH BEFORE LONG, DIGBY, LAD!

HOW'S IT FEEL TO BE CAUGHT IN YOUR OWN TRAP, YOU GREEN GUMP?

QUIT FOOLING, DIGBY! LET'S GET 'EM BACK TO BASE!

POWERED BY THEIR TINY PERSONAL ROCKET-MOTORS, DAN AND DIGBY PROPEL THEIR PRISONERS BACK TO 'SPEEDSTAR'...

GREAT WORK, DAN — AND YOU, TOO, DIGBY!

THE MEKON GAVE US A RUN FOR OUR MONEY, SIR . . .

BUT THE "OLD FIRM" GOT HIM IN THE END!

ALL THAT REMAINS IS TO PICK UP THOSE DESERTERS FROM THE MEKON'S FLEET AND GET BACK TO DEAR OLD EARTH.

WE'VE GOT ASTROSCOPIC BEARINGS ON THE AREA WHERE THEY BALED OUT, SO THE OPERATION SHOULD BE SIMPLE.

FOURPENCE-HALFPENNY

EVERY WEDNESDAY

EAGLE

COMPANION TO GIRL, SWIFT AND ROBIN

6 MAY 1955 Vol. 6 No. 18

DAN DARE
PILOT OF THE FUTURE
PRISONERS OF SPACE

KEEP THOSE PRESS-MEN UNDER CONTROL!

GOOD OLD DAN!

HE'S DONE IT AGAIN!

MY EDITOR'LL FIRE ME IF I DON'T GET A CLOSE-UP OF THE MEKON!

HOORAY!

. THE STORY SO FAR: As 'Speedstar' and 'Elite' squadron touch down at Spacefleet H.Q., Earth is aflame with the thrilling news that Colonel Dan Dare has, at long last, routed the renegade Treens and captured their evil leader, the dread Mekon. Dan Dare, Sir Hubert Guest, Steve Valiant, 'Flamer' Spry, old Groupie and even Xalto – formerly the Mekon's Chief Guard – are world-wide heroes. Reporters and Press photographers surge towards the landing site.

JUST ONE MORE SHOT, COLONEL DARE!

NO COMMENT! AN OFFICIAL STATEMENT WILL BE ISSUED IN DUE COURSE!

RELAX, SIR HUBERT!

WE GO TO PRESS IN HALF-AN-HOUR — WHAT ABOUT A STATEMENT?

WHERE'S THE MEKON?

HOT HEADLINES — LOOK AT THIS LOT!

WHAT A SCOOP!

HOLD IT, DIGBY!

WHAT ABOUT A STATEMENT, MELON-HEAD?

COME ON, MEKKY! A NICE BIG SMILE FOR THE GENTLEMEN OF THE PRESS!

EARTH FOOLS! THEY WILL LIVE TO RUE THE DAY THEY SPARED MY LIFE!

LOOK AT THIS, DIG! I'VE SOUVENIRED THE MEKON'S 'FLYING SAUCEBOAT'!

NO DOUBT THE BOFFINS WILL BAG THAT, FLAMER. I'M OFF TO THE SHOWER-ROOM TO DECONTAMINATE MYSELF!

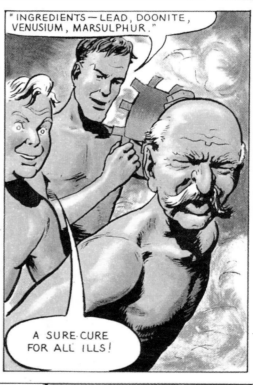

SPECIAL BONUS!
DAN DARE
8 PAGE ADVENTURE
REPRINTED FROM THE
EAGLE
ANNUAL
CHRISTMAS 1954

DAN DARE
PILOT OF THE FUTURE

DAN DARE IS WATCHING A TEST MATCH AT MEKONTA IN HIS QUARTERS AT INTERPLANETARY HQ EARTH

"OPERATION TRICERATOPS"

HAROLD JOHNS & GRETA TOMLINSON

NOW WITH MARAK BOWLING FROM THE RED LAKE END, THE SCORE IS VENUS FOUR HUNDRED AND TWEN———

HERE WE GO AGAIN —MY CALL NUMBER— JUST WHEN IT WAS GETTING EXCITING TOO!

0002

WONDER WHAT THE OLD MAN WANTS THIS TIME.

DARE, I WANT YOU TO MEET SIR NIGEL TAWNY, PRESIDENT OF THE INTERPLANETARY ZOO ON THE ISLE OF WIGHT.

SIR NIGEL HAS A STRANGE COMMISSION FOR US... FRANKLY I'M DOUBTFUL IF WE CAN ACCEPT.

...ALL I ASK IS FOR YOU AND COLONEL DARE TO COME AND SEE WHAT WE'VE PREPARED.

WELL—WE CAN CERTAINLY DO THAT.

THERE'S THE ZOO BLOCK... OVER A THOUSAND INTERPLANETARY FAUNA IN PRESSURISED CAGES.

YOU'VE CERTAINLY GOT IT NICELY LAID OUT, SIR NIGEL.

SO YOU MANAGED TO GET THEM SIR NIGEL!

AH! SO YOU'RE BEHIND THIS, ARE YOU?

I'VE JUST RECEIVED A COUPLE OF MERCURIAN RETRIEVERS!

COME AND SEE THEM!

...AND SO IN DUE COURSE THE HUNTERS APPROACH THE DESOLATE WASTES NEAR THE VENUSIAN FLAME BELT. — HOME OF THE GIANT TRICERATOPS.

HERE, O COLONEL, IS WHERE WE SHOULD MAKE OUR CAMP.

TRACTOR TRANSPORTS RENDEZVOUS ZERO ZERO TWO SIX AND NINER FIFE SEVEN...

SOON WE WILL BE READY COLONEL—MY MECHANICS ARE ASSEMBLING THE NEUTRON GAS GUN, WHICH WILL RENDER THE BEAST UNCONSCIOUS. THESE ARE THE HUNTING CHAIRS.

I SEE — A SORT OF ONE MAN HELICOPTER.

YES—IT IS OPERATED BY A CENTRAL COLUMN—THEY WILL BE CHILD'S PLAY TO YOU COLONEL.

WHOOPS!

HEY, DIG! WAIT FOR ME YOU OLD SPEED HOG!

AUNT ANASTASIA WILL NEVER BELIEVE THIS.

THERE THEY ARE!

YOIKS! TALLY HO!

YOU'VE GOT HIM! NICE WORK DIG.

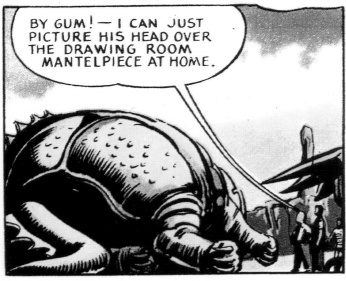

BY GUM! — I CAN JUST PICTURE HIS HEAD OVER THE DRAWING ROOM MANTELPIECE AT HOME.

AH! HERE COMES THE TRANSPORT! — WE'LL START LOADING RIGHT AWAY.

WHEN THE BEAST IS IN POSITION, WE FOLD THE BACK AND SIDES UP TO MAKE AN AIRTIGHT CONTAINER.

THEN, BY GIVING IT DOSES OF GAS, WE ARE ABLE TO KEEP IT UNCONSCIOUS.

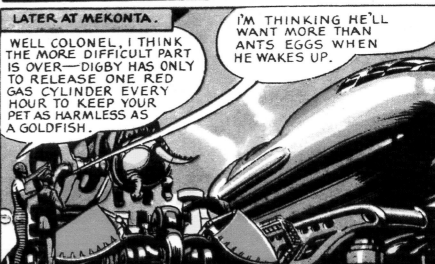

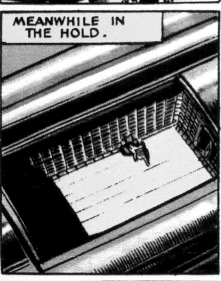

What caused the sirens to wail . . .

their eerie warning over London on the very night Earth was celebrating the triumphant return of Dan Dare and his comrades? . . . Who is the Stranger from Space— and how did he break the light barrier? Don't miss **THE MAN FROM NOWHERE** the new, smash-hit Dan Dare story in next week's 'Eagle'!